4000 Years of Television

4000 Years of Television

THE STORY OF SEEING AT A DISTANCE

by Richard W. Hubbell

G. P. PUTNAM'S SONS, NEW YORK

COPYRIGHT, 1942, BY RICHARD HUBBELL

Designed by Robert Josephy

MANUFACTURED IN THE UNITED STATES OF AMERICA

To Hildegarde and Edmund Canby Gause

CONTENTS

vii

Acknowledgments

MAY I express my appreciation to those members of the Columbia Broadcasting System organization who rendered such valuable assistance—William S. Paley, President; Paul Kesten, Executive Vice-President; Lieutenant Adrian Murphy, United States Army Signal Corps and formerly Executive Director of CBS Television; Leonard H. Hole, acting Executive Director of Television; Peter Goldmark, Chief Television Engineer; Rudolf Bretz, Cameraman-Director who did the drawings for this book; and Agnes Law, Assistant Librarian, and William C. Ackerman, Director of the CBS Reference Library, and Dorothy Shapard.

May I also express my particular thanks to David Sarnoff, President of the Radio Corporation of America; Orrin E. Dunlap, Jr., Manager of the RCA Department of Information; Emil Hijmans of the Philips Export Corporation; John V. L. Hogan, President of the Interstate Broadcasting Company; Harry Stockman of Harvard University and of the Royal Institute of Technology of Stockholm; and Gunnar Hok of New York University and formerly of Svenska Radio A. B. of Sweden.

My thanks and gratitude to James Lawrence Fly, Chairman of the Federal Communications Commission, and to the distinguished Russian-American dancer and choreographer, Adolph Bolm.

And thanks to Kyra Hubbell, for her assistance from start to finish.

I am grateful for permission to use quotations from a number of publications: the British Broadcasting Corporation's *The Listener, BBC Handbook,* and *World-Radio; Fortune; Electronics; Nature;* the *New York Herald Tribune;* the *New York Times;* the *London Times; The Movies Till Now,* by Paul Rotha; *The Outlook For Television,* by Orrin E. Dunlap, Jr.; *Sound Motion Pictures,* by Harold B. Franklin; *Motion Picture Daily; Radio Daily; Radio News; Radio and Television; The Wireless Age; The* (New York) *Sun;* and *Variety.*

PREFACE

I

Demobilization day will find television a fully explored but wholly unexploited field. We can anticipate a widespread demand for consumer goods such as television sets, many factories able and ready to convert back from war production to such consumer goods, and all the other factors necessary for the most rapid postwar television expansion.

I think it quite likely that during the postwar period television will be one of the first industries arising to serve as a cushion against unemployment and depression. Radio broadcasting served that function in a measure during the 1920's, though at the close of the war wireless was far less developed than television will be at the close of this war. There is no reason now apparent why we should not aim at a 50,000,000-set television industry mirroring the present 50,000,000-set standard broadcast industry.

James Lawrence Fly, Chairman
Federal Communications Commission

Washington, D. C.

II

Television—and I include in that term its engineers, its apparatus, its electronics, in fact its whole technical structure—has entered a swift but secret phase of extraordinary development. It is necessarily secret, because television has turned from painting peacetime pictures in quiet living rooms to the lethal job of war. It is swift, this grim new cycle, because it is meeting tomorrow's deadlines today, because it is fighting against time, because a valiant corps of thousands of electronic engineers are working night and day to apply the techniques of television to critical new problems of modern warfare.

In this process, television has been split into a dozen pieces, and each piece is receiving the kind of concentrated development and elaboration which the whole has previously received. How those pieces will be reassembled into peacetime television after we have won the war, what pattern they will form, what radical changes they will bring about, no one can prophesy today. It is my personal belief, however, that this wartime development will revolutionize our peacetime television pictures. That is likewise the opinion of our entire staff of laboratory engineers who are devoting their energies and time to military projects for the National Defense Research Committee.

Thus, whatever promises television has held, as a social force to conjure with, should be given added sweep and power when its deadly military skills are recombined into the peacetime arts of entertainment and education. Pictures of richer detail and precision, pictures in a full panoply of natural color instead of merely black and white, receiving sets of lower cost and surprising compactness—all these may well result. And we the broadcasters, as well as you the future audience, may properly enjoy every improvement in television which emerges from this wartime work, not only with pleasure, but with national pride.

William S. Paley
President, Columbia Broadcasting System
New York City

III

Television will bring to the home a complete means of instantaneous participation in the sights and sounds of the outer world. Radio has already shown the great psychological impact on the listener of feeling himself present at a radio performance. In television, the combined emotional results of both seeing and hearing an event as it occurs becomes a new force of great significance. Experienced in the intimate background of one's home, it is a far more powerful force than anything we have yet known.

Sociologists have pointed to the immense potentialities of propaganda in television. The great mass of the human race is often swayed by appeals to emotion rather than to reason. Millions of people in countries which have succumbed to dictatorships have undergone extraordinary changes in their expressed actions and beliefs. These changes have been wrought in a short time, with the aid of radio propaganda. Vast populations have been led to accept ideologies contrary to their former beliefs, because of skillfully presented ideas, which were spread with the speed of light into every home of those unfortunate lands.

With the advent of television, it has become even more important than before that we preserve our precious right to freedom of discussion—and guard television against exploitation in transmitting propaganda intended to arouse racial animosities, religious hatreds, and destructive class struggles.

Television's ultimate contribution can be its role in the betterment of the life of the nation, and, at the same time, the greater development of the life of the individual.

We, who have labored in the development of this ultimate form of communication, are proud to have the opportunity to aid in the progress of mankind. It is our earnest hope that television will help to strengthen the United States as a nation of free people and high ideals, in war and in peace.

David Sarnoff

President, Radio Corporation of America

New York City

IV

When, as a young man, I came to the United States on that first tour of the Ballets Russes of Serge Diaghileff, there was not only no television but no sound radio broadcasting, either. The dancer, the actor, the musician, the singer, and the painter presented their art in the theater, in personal appearance. But, even then, the actor had begun to find a new world in the movies. Musician and singer had begun to find a vast new audience in those scratchy, old-fashioned phonographs. With the advent of radio their world was revolutionized, expanded to gigantic proportions.

The dancer, the choreographer, and the painter were not given such an opportunity. Working in a visual medium, they were unable to use vision-less radio and phonograph records. Built largely on highly specialized movement, on color, and on the psychological impact of actual presence, of living personal appearance, the role of the dancer has been essentially a limited one in black and white photoplays. This has been primarily the world of the actor and playwright.

In television, however, there *is*, to an amazing extent, that sense of actuality. You *know* there is a living performance actually taking place before your eyes at that very instant. In addition, television offers color, with ease, with fidelity, without entailing a back-breaking production budget.

Television opens a world of new opportunities to artists in every field—but to the dancer, the choreographer, and the painter it offers something unique. To these, television can be what the radio and the modern phonograph have been to the musician, the singer, the composer.

The development of television introduces a force of unparalleled power, not only to the world of art, but ultimately to every walk of life. The changes that will come about as a result of being able to extend vision over great distances are almost beyond imagination.

Adolph Bolm

Hollywood, California

4000 Years of Television

More Than a Magic Carpet

HISTORY and the progress of civilization have always been indissolubly linked with man's ability to *communicate* with his fellow men. To communicate—to send ideas, thoughts, and information from one person to another.

In lands where there was no communication with the rest of the world, there was no progress. Isolated tribes in the interior of Africa, completely cut off from other peoples, still live under prehistoric conditions.

Where man did learn to communicate with others, ideas and discoveries were exchanged; cultures flourished. With each new method of communication, the march towards civilization advanced a step. Each improvement played its part in the building, and sometimes the destruction, of nations.

Man has always searched for better ways to communicate. Down through the ages he has searched, always improving on older forms, until he reached the most powerful, the most rapid and complete method of all—television. Perhaps a century or two from now, historians will write that it changed our twentieth-century world as much as the invention of gunpowder or the airplane, the telephone or the automobile.

Hundreds of fantastic yarns have already been circulated about its "magic power," but how many people really *know* the facts about this powerful new influence which may alter our lives profoundly?

What is television?

Where did it come from?

How can it change your life?

What can you expect from it?

What is it? The very name is a clue. Tele-vision—a student of Greek and Latin will tell you it means "seeing-at-a-distance." *Seeing at a distance!*

It was created by man's most insatiable characteristic —curiosity. We all want to know what is happening next door. There is a touch of the keyhole-peeper in all of us.

Man is so curious he wanted what all the best wizards, magicians, and assorted astrologers have been unable to do since the beginning of time. He wanted even more than a magic carpet. He wanted to be in two places at one time.

What man wanted was television.

Of course, magicians have tried to find out what was going on in their neighbors' houses by peering into crystal balls. But, try as they might, none of them ever turned out a crystal ball which could do a satisfactory job.

Man had to wait centuries, until he learned about optics, magnetism, electronics, astronomy, metallurgy, chemistry, and a thousand other things. Television was not invented overnight. It is a product of the accumulated knowledge of thousands of wise men, in many lands, in many centuries.

To achieve television, the power of seeing at a distance, meant the perfection of a machine—a machine to duplicate the powers of the eye and ear. More than this, it must traverse great distances in a split second.

This was the goal to be reached.

Before the story begins, let us take a glance at this goal and see what it involves. Actually, it involves quite a staggering amount, even though it may seem fairly simple in this drawing:

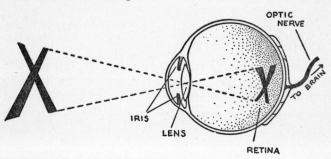

Rays of light shine on an object—in this case a simple X mark. From the X the light is reflected into the viewer's eye.

This *image* of reflected light, this "picture" of the X mark goes into the eye through the *pupil*. The pupil is the opening in the center of the *iris*.

This iris is that circular part of the eye which may be colored blue or brown or gray. If it is blue, we say a person has blue eyes. The iris has the job of regulating the amount of light that gets into the eye. When it is dark, the iris automatically opens wide to let in all available light. In bright sunshine it closes to a small opening so that too much light will not enter and dazzle you.

Next the image passes through the *lens*, a section of elastic, transparent material.

Automatically controlled by tiny muscles, the *lens* focuses the image on the "back wall" of the eye, in the manner of a movie projector focusing a picture on the wall of a room.

This "back wall" is called the *retina*. It is studded with the ends of thousands upon thousands of tiny nerves of a very special type. When light falls on them, they are stimulated, and in each one a tiny electric *"nerve current"* is created.

These sight nerves run out of the back of the retina and are tied together in one big bundle—called the optic nerve. The electric nerve currents, which are an electrical recording of the *image* of the X mark, run through this bundle of nerves to the brain. There the brain transforms them into the sensation which we call "sight" or "vision."

At this very moment then, as you read this, the light is being reflected from the page into your eye, carrying with it the picture of these printed words. Through the pupil, through the lens, and the image is focused on the retina with its nerve endings. There the image is converted into hundreds of thousands of tiny electric impulses which travel through as many nerves direct to the brain, where they are seen all at once.

Very briefly, that is how your eye, the human *camera*, works.

Since the word *camera* has appeared already, let us note in passing that in this book it will be used in its modern application—any sort of device that can see or take any kind of picture. This will simplify matters. It is also the word used in modern television studios.

Now look at the drawing of the ear. Your ear, my ear, anybody's ear.

First we need a noise. Bang your hand on the table, but not too hard. There—we have a noise.

When you struck the table, you made it *vibrate*. That made the air around it vibrate, too. Those vibrations in the air traveled out in all directions. Similarly, if you drop a pebble in a pool of water, little ripples go out in all directions.

Some of these vibrations, or *sound waves*, were caught by your outer ear. Those curiously shaped things on either side of your head which you call your ears are really your *outer ears*. Their job is that of an ear trumpet, to scoop up the sound waves and direct them inside to the "auditory canal"—the hole in the ear. That is why we cup one hand behind an ear when we want to hear better. It makes our "hearing trumpet" bigger and catches more sound waves.

Stretched tightly across the end of the "auditory canal" is a thin membrane, like the head of a drum. In fact, it is called the *eardrum*, and when the sound waves reach it, they make it vibrate, too. This starts a little chain of bones vibrating in the middle ear, and they pass the vibrations along to a second eardrum, stretched over the entrance to the inner ear.

The inner ear is irregular in shape, with a complicated series of canals filled with liquid—as you can see in the drawing. Sticking out into this liquid, from the walls of the canals, are thousands of minute nerve endings.

When the inner eardrum vibrates, it transmits the vibrations to the fluid, which carries them along to the ends of these nerves. The nerves are tickled by the vibrations. So much so that little currents are created in each nerve.

These nerve currents are an electrical record of the sound vibrations, and they pass through "wires," the

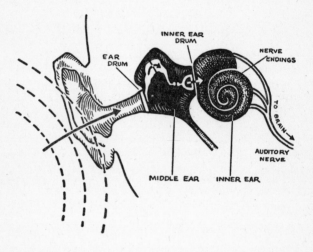

auditory nerves, to the brain. Here they are transformed into the sensation we call hearing.

Summing up, when you struck your hand on the table, you started a series of vibrations which were passed through the air into your ear to the nerve endings. They were converted into nerve currents and sent to your brain, where they were "heard."

In brief, that is the way you hear.

To create *electric* eyes and ears as good as these was a long, hard task. But, generations of scientists stuck to the job, and the story of how man learned to hear and see at a distance is a fascinating one. It is a story of time and space annihilated, telescoped into the pulse beat of an electron.

It is a story of forces which can create or consume entire nations.

It is the story of an almost magic power, growing like a genie in our midst. A power which people have not yet known.

This is the story of television.

CHAPTER ONE

The Story Begins

THE STORY begins thousands of years ago, before the dawn of history. We have no written records of this prehistoric age, only comparatively few traces. From these we can conjecture what may have taken place.

The Ice Age was ending. The frozen shell which had gripped the world was melting away. Only in the extreme north and south—the arctic and antarctic—did desolate wastes of snow and ice remain throughout the year.

Imagine five or six hulking figures crouched in a cave. They were men and women, although they looked more like apes. Their skins were rough, covered with coarse hair. Their bodies, squat and heavy.

These were cavemen, remote ancestors of ours. Only a little removed from the apes of the forest, they had no clothes to keep them warm, no home but a cave. Shivering in the cold, they crouched around one man, their leader, who had learned how to control them. At first he had done it only by the strength of his arm. Yet there were things he could not express with a club. He wanted them to understand what he was beginning to think about, and he found that by making certain gestures and grunting in special ways he could make his companions understand.

If they did what he wished, he could grunt again—more softly—to show he was pleased. If they did not obey, he could still get his way by using a club.

This caveman had instinctively learned to *communicate* with others, to express his thoughts. He had conveyed information to others.

When this happened, something else probably happened, too. The other cave-dwellers gathered around him, followed where he led, obeyed his commands. It was the first tribe, the first time primitive men had gathered together of their own free will into a common group, a community. It was the first little nation.

All this happened because one caveman, more intelligent than the others, communicated his "intelligence" to his fellow cavemen. Because he could do this, he became their leader, and a tribe was formed.

The story begins here because this is also the beginning of the history of mankind and of communication —the beginning of the long march towards something called civilization. Its advance depended on the ability of successive generations to express themselves and communicate with others.

Tens of centuries went by. The cavemen became more expressive and learned to combine two grunts of different pitch—making it possible to express two things at a time.

More centuries passed by, and they had built up a crude form of speech.

Imagine how one day a hunter might have returned to the cave with fresh meat, two wolves he had killed with his stone ax. While his friends tore the raw flesh apart, the hunter leaned against the wall of the cave, examining his crude weapon.

He decided to make it sharper, to remove the blunt edge by rubbing it against the stone wall. The soft sandstone gave way to the hardness of the flint axhead, leaving marks on the wall.

That amused him and he scratched again, and again, until, almost without realizing it, he had made a crude drawing of a man.

The others, chewing on their wolf meat, came to see what he was doing. The hunter stepped back to admire his work and explained, in grunt language, what it was.

His friends understood and grunted their approval.

Now even a primitive caveman likes to be flattered. It made him feel important, and he scratched away some more, making what passed for a wolf.

More compliments, until he felt positively dynamic. So dynamic that he drew a second wolf. Inspiration followed. If he were such a clever fellow, why not make sure that everyone knew it. He changed the picture again, putting an ax in the man's hand, and having it descend on the wolf's head.

Turning to the circle of admiring friends, he explained this man was himself, being a brave and important person.

The friends were terribly impressed. They grunted and danced about in delight. They patted the hunter on the back, and he felt better and better all the time. After a while he felt so important he might be described as the first "big shot" in history. Next day he tried more drawings. As time went on he continued his career as the first artist and the first writer.

For the first time people had looked at a flat surface and seen symbols and pictures which conveyed information to them. Man was beginning to record history and knowledge. From these crude drawings sprang writing and painting—new ways to communicate. Before very long the artist was head man not only around his own cave but throughout the entire neighborhood.

Early men learned other things, too. When they wanted to send a message to a tribe on the next mountain, they had to walk across the valley and wade through the river. In springtime the river was swollen with rain and melting snow. It was too deep and too cold to wade. One man, perhaps, noticed something. Logs floated on the surface of the water. Catching one, he sat upon it and eventually drifted across to the other side. Here was the first boat!

A slow business, but he soon learned to make the log go where he wanted by kicking his feet and scooping with his hands. It was only a matter of time until someone picked up a flat stick and pushed at the water with it, inventing the paddle. As the centuries rolled on, other men learned to harness the wind to their boats. The sailboat was "invented" when some curious navigator took off his wolf-skin tunic and held it up to the breeze.

Primitive men live in fear, and when the lightning flashed and thunder boomed they trembled in their caves. When the earth shook and mountains spewed forth rivers of flowing lava, the cavemen fled in terror. For when this happened a horrible demon came racing through the forest. Sinister and evil, its lurid red breath consumed everything in its path. This was the fire demon, more deadly than the saber-tooth tiger.

But primitive men learned to tame the fire demon, to make it serve them, keep them warm, cook food, and keep the animals at bay. When the sun had set and night closed in, it lighted up the darkness so men could see.

A man could carry fire in a torch and walk safely through the forest at night. He could send a message as far as the next mountain top. By day he heaped wet leaves upon a fire, after the fashion of the American Indians, who spelled out messages in puffs of smoke. By night, he climbed to the top of a high rock and waved a flaming brand back and forth. Other men across the valley would see his signal of fire and wave back their answer in words of flame.

In another tribe, an old woman might have been curing the skins of animals, drying them in the sun. She stretched a hide across the end of a hollow, burned-out tree stump, pinning it down on the sharp splinters.

Hours later, when she returned, the skin had shrunken tight across the top of the stump, like a drumhead. The old woman examined it curiously, tapped it with a finger. It made a rumbling, grumbling sound. She tapped it harder, with a stick. It gave a pulsating boom, strangely pleasing. She struck it again and again, and the harder she struck, the louder this first drum boomed.

Imagine how the men of the tribe might have come running to investigate. Head-man, who was hunting in the next valley, heard it, too, even at so great a distance.

He decided that henceforth when he wished to summon the tribesmen together or send a message to a friend he would do it by pounding on a drum. This was much easier, and quicker, than carrying a message on foot.

Uncounted centuries were passing, and the march towards civilization progressed another step, and another. Boats, writing, drawing, fire, drums—each improvement played its part.

Somewhere in the remote interior of Asia, roving tribes learned to tame the horse. Upon its back a warrior could overtake the fastest runner and cover ten times the distance he could on foot. Fierce Mongols, mounted on their horses, swept their enemies before them.

Later on, in times of peace, the horse was put to better use. Caravans were formed, using horses, donkeys, and camels. They journeyed thousands of miles, from Turkestan to China, from Egypt to Assyria and Persia. Merchants and soldiers, armed with bronze swords and shields of burnished copper, brought home new discoveries, new ideas, new knowledge.

These men were curious. They crossed every horizon to find what lay beyond. They traversed burning, parched deserts and ice-bound mountain passes. They sailed unknown seas in frail boats. They were determined to find out what it was like on the other side even though the way was long and hard and dangerous.

If only they could see what was going on "over there" without wasting days or months or years in travel.

CHAPTER TWO

3580 B.C.

DATES do not mean very much in themselves. They are just numbers. When certain information is tacked onto a date, we know that such and such a thing happened at that time.

But dates are useful in one respect. They provide us with a sort of framework on which to hang our knowledge. We can peg out our facts in the right order, tying them to hitching posts. It helps to keep things straight in our own minds.

As we leave the Age of Unrecorded History and enter that small portion of the past of which we have some record, let us peg down our facts with a date here and there. We are going to cover another 5500 years, and a lot of things can happen in fifty-five centuries.

Our first peg is the year 3580 before Christ. In that year began the reign of King Assa, who ruled over Egypt from 3580 until 3536, B.C.

Probably the oldest known relic of *paper* is a document which gives the accounts of the reign of King Assa of Egypt, beginning in 3580 B.C. This is not paper as we know it today, but "papyrus paper." Papyrus is the name of a reed, widely cultivated in ancient Egypt. Thin layers of the stem were peeled off, flattened out, and pressed together to form paper-like sheets. Its importance is this—it was the first durable, satisfactory form of writing "paper." Without such a writing material, early scholars would have had an even more difficult task than they did in recording their knowledge for future generations to study. It would have been almost impossible to disseminate and preserve knowledge. Before the introduction of papyrus, scholars had to use soft wax tablets which melted in the sun or rough animal skins or blocks of stone or wood or clumsy tablets of clay. None of these, as you might suspect, was particularly satisfactory.

After the decline of Egypt, the use of papyrus was almost forgotten, for in Europe it was not grown. Parchment became the principal writing material of the scholar. More expensive than papyrus, parchment is the specially prepared and specially cured skin of goats, calves, and sheep. Paper, as we know it today, was not introduced in Europe until late in the eleventh century A.D.

The advent of papyrus paper, in the period around 3580 B.C., is noted here because it was a highly important development in methods of communication. It was the first reasonably good writing material. Scholars could now record their knowledge in permanent form with comparative ease. This was an advance as important in history as its companion improvement, the introduction of the printing press. But that was not to be invented for another 5000 years.

Now for our second date peg. We go fifteen centuries ahead. Here we meet one of the three cornerstones of television—the first example of the practical use of what eventually became the science of optics—the study of light, of vision, of seeing.

Primitive men must have learned some things about light. It is doubtful, though, that they thought about it very much. Yet those who did notice that light travels in a straight line only must have been puzzled. Why? Because light could be made to go around a corner—by *reflecting* it from a shiny surface or by *refracting* (bending) it by passing it through water, rock crystal, or quartz.

We know that in some ancient civilizations wise men puzzled about the image of themselves which they saw on the surface of a pool of water or on the gleaming surface of a copper shield. It is futile, though, to guess just when ancient men understood they could see an *image* of themselves in this fashion. It took little ingenuity or inventiveness to look at a pond.

But we have found something, as early as 2000 B.C., which did require considerable inventive ability. Towards the end of the last century, an archeologist was digging in the ruins of the Palace of Nimrod in ancient Assyria, about which we read in the Old Testament of the Bible. He unearthed a convex-shaped lens of rock crystal. It was so fashioned that as the rays of sunlight passed through it they were bent, or *refracted*, together. When they were concentrated on one small spot, it became so hot that bits of tinder, dried grass, and wood shavings placed there would catch fire.

You can do the same thing with a common magnifying glass. Hold it between your hand and the sun, so the light is concentrated on one small spot. You will soon feel why it can start a fire.

The Assyrians used this slow but sure ancestor of the cigarette lighter about 4000 years ago—around the year 2000 B.C. But, as the centuries rolled on, there were wars, and Assyria was destroyed, forgotten. The Assyrians' knowledge of *optics*, of *reflecting* mirrors, and *refracting* "sun glasses" or lenses, was buried in the ruins of Nimrod.

The Greeks, and the Romans after them, learned something about optics, too. The Greeks, however, were inclined toward theory and, on the whole, less interested in testing by detailed, organized research.*

The Greeks found theories to explain light, why things could be seen, and why they appeared to be colored. These theories dominated all thought about optics until the end of the eighteenth century A.D.—only 150 years ago.

Beyond the theory stage the Greeks did not go. Failing to test their ideas and put them to work, nothing very much happened to this cornerstone of television. That being the case, let us put optics aside for a thousand years or so. We will bump into it again later on.

Our next peg is on the year 800 B.C.

* Aristophanes speaks of a "sun glass" or "burning glass," to melt away the writing on a wax tablet, in his play, *Clouds*, written about 424 B.C.

Euclid is credited with the authorship of two treatises on optics and vision, dated around 300 B.C.

Cleomedes, around 50 A.D., in his *Cyclical Theory of Meteors* gives examples of refraction or the bending of light. He talks, for instance, of the apparent bending of a stick when it is partly submerged in water.

The most celebrated of the early writers on optics was Ptolemy, of Alexandria—second century A.D. He is thought to have been the author of a very comprehensive analysis of the nature of light and color.

Hero, of Alexandria, who built the first steam engine, also experimented in optics.

If you will look at a map of ancient Greece, you will find a district called Magnesia near the Aegean Sea. As long ago as eight hundred years before the birth of Christ, the natives there carried on a mildly thriving trade in magic—magic stones, to be exact.

They used to find a most unusual kind of very heavy rock. When a piece of iron was brought near it, the iron would stick to the stone. Most irregular, thought the ancient Greeks. It must be magic!

Actually what they had found was a form of iron ore which behaved exactly like one of our present day magnets—available in any five and ten cent store for five cents. In fact, because these "rocks" were found in great quantities in the district of Magnesia, the Greeks called them "magnes" or Magnesian stones.*

In recent centuries we have called the magnes stone by different names. In Jules Verne's novel, *A Journey to the Center of the Earth*, it is called the "lodestone"—a stone that leads.

Today we have a more familiar name—*magnetite*, and pieces of this "iron-ore-which-attracts" are called *magnets*. The branch of science devoted to the study of magnets is called *magnetism*.

More than mere trinkets, the ancient Magnesians found something upon which the entire science of electricity—with all its grandchildren—was to be established twenty-four centuries later.

After the Greek-Roman civilization was destroyed by barbarians from northern Europe, there followed the Dark Ages. A thousand years of ignorance, in which

---

* A number of Greek writers, after 800 B.C., have mentioned it—Homer, Plato, Aristotle, and Theophrastus. The Roman poet, Lucretius, speaks of it in his *De Rerum Natura*.

science was blacked out and the progress of civilization turned back. In the entire 2400 years between the eighth century B.C. and the end of the sixteenth century A.D., only three things were learned about the magnet.

First—it would attract certain metals, such as iron.

Second—when a piece of iron is touched by a magnet, it becomes temporarily "magnetized"—turned into a temporary magnet and capable of attracting other pieces of iron.

Third—what every Boy Scout knows, the principle of the mariner's compass. A magnet in the shape of a needle, balanced on a pivot so it is free to swing around on a horizontal plane, will always turn to one position. It will point to the north. Christopher Columbus sailed across the ocean and discovered America guided only by his mariner's compass and a mariner's astrolabe for reading the position of the sun.

The ancient Chinese may have known this principle of the compass as early as 1100 B.C. Possibly they deserve credit for using magnets three hundred years before the Greeks began to find the Magnesian stone. But whoever discovered the principle of the compass, it was not known in western Europe until the eleventh or twelfth century A.D.

Until the end of the sixteenth century A.D., nothing more was learned. Of course, people concocted strange ideas about magnets, or lodestones, and spun many yarns about them. Some of these were published in London, in the year 1600, by the Gilbert Club.

One writer declared, "If a lodestone be annointed with garlic, or if a diamond be near, it does not attract iron."

"If pickled in the salt of a suckling fish, there is

power to pick up gold which has fallen into the deepest wells."

Others announced there were "various kinds of magnets, some of which attract gold." A premature Izaak Walton even proclaimed there were lodestones which could attract fish.

Magnetism puttered along like this until a certain Englishman published a remarkable book in 1600. The author was the father of modern electricity, and his name was William Gilbert.

The Greeks made one more discovery, which forms the third cornerstone of today's television. It was a discovery as mixed up with magic as the Magnesian stone. In fact, it remained in the class of magic tricks until recent times. Our peg for this is placed at the year 640 B.C.

It was then that a learned Greek philosopher, Thales of Miletus, was born. Thales was one of the seven "wise men of Greece," and before his demise in 546 B.C. he had his finger in a great many things.

He was the founder of Greek geometry, astronomy, and philosophy. He was even able to stop a war.

Shortly after 590 B.C., Thales told his friends there would be a total eclipse of the sun in 585 B.C. When that year came along, two of the Greek city states were having a war between themselves. On the 28th of May, 585 B.C., right in the middle of a blitzkrieg, the sun disappeared in eclipse. The two armies were so impressed that they took Thales' advice and called off the war. They went even further and became friendly.

Then, not to be outdone by the Magnesians, Thales and his fellow countrymen began to find magic stones.

These stones were different from the magnes stone and much more chic. A brownish-yellow in color and very light in weight, they were ideal for jewelry.

They were so light that sometimes when Thales was at the seaside he would find pieces washed up on the beach.

These stones were transparent and floated in water! Very strange! Still more unusual, you would sometimes find little bugs and flies entombed in them, as in a cake of brown ice. And if you threw the stones into a fire, they burned!

Thales and his friends were most intrigued, and they held them up to the light to peer through them. Cleaning off the sand and grit, Thales rubbed his stone against his woolen cloak.

Then the real magic began. Bits of fluff on the cloak, specks of dust, and bits of dried grass began to stick to the stone. Even the whiskers in his beard prickled up and stuck to it.

Thales had no idea why it happened. It just did. Therefore, it must be magic. The next time Thales had some writing to do, he had a few words to say about the new magical stone, which he named *Elektron*.

Today we call this stone *amber* and use it for jewelry and ornaments. Sometimes we find flies entombed in it, too. Quite understandable, for amber was originally sap oozing out of a tree. A fly could easily land in it, get stuck, and be covered over as the sap hardened. After countless ages had passed, the sap petrified, turned into stone, which we call amber.

Amber, or Elektron, as Thales called it, acquires a charge of static electricity when rubbed. In the same way, when we scuff our shoes across a thick rug on a winter day and touch a lamp, we have a spark jump from our finger tips to the metal fixture. When amber acquires an electric charge, it attracts and picks up dust, fluff, paper, straw, and hair.

Aside from its so-called magical powers, nothing more was learned of the properties of amber and the reasons for its strange behavior until 1600 A.D.

When we reach that "peg" we shall again hear of Mr. William Gilbert, who investigated not only magnets, but also amber, or Elektron, as it was called then. Gilbert studied other stones which had the same power as amber. These he called "electrics," "things which attract for the same reason that Elektron or amber does."

Our familiar words *"electric"* and the science of "electrics," which is called *"electricity,"* go back nearly 2600 years to ancient Greece, when wise old Thales of Miletus christened amber with the name "Elektron."

In honor of this, in 1891 A.D., the name of *electron* was given to the smallest known thing in the world, that smallest natural unit of electricity which is a tiny part of an atom. From the study of the electron came the branch of science which produced today's television— *electronics.*

Optics, magnetism, and electronics—the three foundation stones of television. They had their beginnings long ago, but eager as men were to find a way to see at a distance and be in two places at one time, the three cornerstones remained unrecognized and unused for thousands of years.

Unused until one man started the ball rolling and began a chain of events that lasted for 350 years. Then optics, magnetism, and electronics joined hands and amazing things began to happen.

CHAPTER THREE

Alhazen the Arab, and William Gilbert, Esq.

THE last chapter ended on the date peg of 640 B.C. This chapter winds up at 1600 A.D. It is a big jump —twenty-two hundred and forty years—and it has a number of interesting events, events which were not actual cornerstones of television but which did have a direct bearing on it.

During the fourth century B.C., in the city of Tarentum, Greece, there lived the philosopher Archytas, a very intimate friend of Plato. This gifted Hellene was versatile—a statesman, general, flute-player, scientist, inventor of the children's rattle, as well as a mathematician, musician, and acoustical engineer. He led a highly useful life until he was eighty-one, when, in 347 B.C., his career was cut short by drowning.

Archytas built the first "flying machine." It was a wooden pigeon which moved by compressed air—"So nicely was it balanced by weights and put in motion by hidden and enclosed air," as Aulus Gellius wrote of it. This "hidden and enclosed air" may have made the pigeon the first example of a hot-air balloon—for which two Frenchmen, the Montgolfier brothers, will formally get the credit twenty-two hundred years from this point.

If anyone were to ask you who built the first steam engine, the chances are you would answer, "James Watt." Actually, you would be wrong by about nineteen hundred years. A scientist named Hero, of Alexandria, Egypt, built the first steam engine in recorded history around 130 B.C. He used it to open temple doors and spray water in fountains.

About the same time, the Chinese were learning how to make real paper, an art unknown outside of China for the next nine hundred years.

Going ahead those nine centuries brings us to the eighth century A.D., to the city of Samarkand, in what is now the Uzbek Soviet Socialist Republic—part of Russian Turkestan. On a world map, you will find it just north of Afghanistan.

In 712, A.D., the Arabs occupied Samarkand. Forty years later they were attacked by the Chinese, whom they defeated. A number of Chinese were taken prisoner. Some of the captives were skilled paper-makers, and they passed their knowledge on to the Arabs.

When the Arabs moved westward toward Europe, they brought paper with them. It first appeared in Greece around the end of the eleventh century, but after the Arabs fell from power, the science of paper-making declined in the hands of the unskilled Europeans. Not until the last quarter of the thirteenth century did it develop. In 1276 the first large paper mills were set up at Fabriano, in the marquisate of Ancona, Italy.

Paper, easier to make and handle than parchment, provided our civilization with an inexpensive material on which to record its knowledge. It was a great step forward, an improved method of communication, which, in turn, contributed to the progress of civilization. Only two centuries more and we shall have the printing press!

The first flying machine, the first steam engine, and the invention of paper. None directly connected with television, yet each has a place in the story. Each one attests to man's will to progress. Each is a milestone in history and a block in the structure of knowledge out of which television grew.

When that great wave of ignorance which we call the Dark Ages engulfed Europe, schools and academies were closed. Communications between provinces broke down, progress ceased, and western civilization withered away, to hibernate in isolated monasteries.

Far to the east an amazing civilization was flourishing—in China. Unfortunately, it was thousands of miles away, beyond endless deserts, the highest mountains, and the longest wall in the world—barriers penetrated by only a few adventurous explorers. It was not the Chinese who preserved the knowledge of the Greeks and Romans after their civilization had crumbled. It was the Arabs.

When the Arabs rose to power under Mohammed in the seventh century, they inherited the treasure of Greek culture. For five hundred years they preserved and increased its measure in science and in art.

The greatest of the Arabian scientists was born in Basra, near the mouth of the Tigris and Euphrates Rivers. He was Abu Ali Al-Hasan Ibn Alhasan. (He died in Cairo, in 1038 A.D.)

This fellow is known in history by the somewhat

more easily handled name of Alhazen. He first attracted attention to himself by boasting long and loud that he could build a machine to regulate the periodic floods of the Nile River in Egypt. He talked until people began to take him seriously—much as a politician gets himself elected to office by telling the public, over and over, how wonderful he is.

Finally, the Caliph Hakim decided to send him to Egypt to build his machine, which put Alhazen on the Arabian spot. He knew perfectly well his bluff would be discovered. He knew just as well that angry caliphs were in the habit of removing the heads of those who irritated them. There being only one smart way out, he took it. He was also a good actor, and before the day of departure arrived, the Caliph was informed that poor Alhazen had lost his mind.

Alhazen kept up the bluff until the old Caliph died. Then he went back to work—doing less talking and producing more results.

One result which interests us particularly was his examination of the human eye and his explanation of its workings.

Before Alhazen's time scientists believed men could see because the eye sent out invisible rays like a searchlight. What is important for television, Alhazen declared this was all wrong. He said vision was made possible by rays coming *from* the object at which one looked. These rays *entered* the eye and enabled you to see.

Alhazen also wrote about magnifying lenses, and it is quite possible that his work inspired the invention of eyeglasses, credited to Friar Bacon two centuries later.

While the Arabs were preserving and adding to the

general fund of knowledge, the backward countries of Europe began to struggle up from the morass of the Dark Ages.

In the thirteenth century, the Arabian state of the Caliph of Bagdad was destroyed by two more or less barbaric invaders, the Crusaders from Europe and the Mongols from central Asia.

The knowledge and books of the Arabs were transferred to Europe after the Crusaders came. In 1270 A.D., the first treatise on optics was written by a European, the Polish scientist Vitello. He based his work on that of the Alexandrian Ptolemy (second century A.D.) and Alhazen. Incidentally, the book was not "published" until three centuries later—it had to wait for the invention of printing, which it preceded by 170 years.

A contemporary of Vitello was the English scientist and philosopher, Roger Bacon (*circa* 1214-*circa* 1294). The scientific training which Bacon received at Oxford was mainly a study of the Arab writers.

The only records we have of Bacon's inventions are his writings, in which he was not too explicit. In those days it was dangerous to invent a new gadget—such as a telescope. The all-powerful church might regard you as a magician, in league with the devil. Indeed, Friar Bacon, although a member of the Franciscan order, suffered at the hands of jealous colleagues who were all too eager to regard him as a fellow traveler with the powers of darkness.

Bacon invented, or worked out, the principles of the magic lantern, spectacles, the telescope, and the microscope. His study of the various uses of the lens lifted the science of optics several rungs up the ladder.

The idea of flying, as a means of communication, was tickling men's imaginations in those days. Friar Bacon, for instance, thought out a most ingenious—if impractical—airship. He designed a large metal globe which was to be filled with a hypothetical lighter-than-air substance designated as "ethereal air," or "liquid fire." Being lighter than air, it was supposed to make the metal globe and its attached basket float in the air. There is no record of its ever having been built.

Then there is an old legend which tells how an English monk named Elmerus flew from a town in Spain for a distance of more than a furlong, in the time of Edward the Confessor (King of England, 1040-1066). Giovanni Battista Dante, of Perugia, Italy, was said to have flown across Lake Trasimeno several times. Albert of Saxony (Bishop of Halberstadt, 1366-1390) designed an airship something like Bacon's.

At the beginning of the sixteenth century, an Italian alchemist in Galloway, Scotland, tried to fly from the walls of Stirling Castle all the way to France. When he took off, instead of landing in France he pancaked into a near-by pile of manure and broke his thigh bone. He explained the accident: the wings he used contained some chicken feathers, which had an "affinity" for the dung hill. Whereas, had they been composed solely of eagles' feathers, they would have been attracted to the air.

Well, only four hundred years more till the Wright Brothers.

About this time we come to a man named Johann Gutenberg, who was experimenting with a new way to print words. By 1440, Gutenberg's invention of movable type became generally known in the city of Strasbourg. His invention, the printing press, made books and printed material available, in time, throughout the world.

To be sure, newspapers of a sort had been seen long before this. The earliest ones were bulletins carved on stone slabs and displayed in the market places of ancient Assyria and Babylon. In the Roman Empire there was the *Acta Diurna* or "Daily Events," official bulletins copied by scribes and delivered to subscribers in the provinces.

After Gutenberg invented the printing press, small pamphlets and single sheet journals appeared from time to time, without any regularity. In 1562, a hand-written official paper, the *Notizie Scritte* was published every month in Venice. It was displayed in a public place, and a small fee was charged those who read it. The fee was an Italian coin, called a *gazzetta*. From this came the word gazette, so often used in names of newspapers today.

It was not until 1609 that the first regularly published newspaper appeared in Germany. The first English paper, *The Weekly Newes from Italy, Germany, etc.* appeared in 1622. There is an old story that the word "news" came from the four letters on the points of a compass—N-E-W-S (north, east, west, south). A compass was printed on early newspapers to show their stories were gathered from the four points of the compass, from great distances.

Leonardo da Vinci was a man of such wide and amazing talents we should not be surprised to find him in the family tree of television. He gets his place, in 1472, by being one of the earlier people, in comparatively modern times, to investigate a useful weakness of the human eye.* Useful, because it makes television and motion pictures work.

Have you ever noticed that when an electric fan begins to revolve you can distinguish the separate blades only for a moment—while it is going very slowly. Then it all becomes a blur, though the individual blades are still there. Or, on the Fourth of July, have you ever watched someone light a "sparkler" and wave it around in a circle? It looks like a complete ring of fire though it is actually just one small flame.

This happens because your eye sees something different from what actually exists—an illusion. Today the illusion is called *persistence of vision*. Vision which persists—pictures which hang around in your eye for a split second overtime.

Remember, in the Prologue, we talked about the human eye and the "sight nerves" which studded the "back wall," or retina, of the eye? The sight nerves, sensitive to light, pick up the scene at which you are looking and send it to the brain.

These sight nerves, each one a miniature "electric eye," do not send all of the picture at one shot. In effect, they "remember" it for a split second afterwards, and although the picture has grown weaker they "echo," they "repeat" and send the same picture to the brain again.

For this reason, if an object is moving rapidly, your eye may see it in two places at the same time. As you

* Leonardo da Vinci was not the first—by many centuries. As early as 65 B.C. it was discussed by Titus Lucretius Carus in *De Rerum Natura*, Lib. IV.

watch a revolving propeller, you see the blades first in one position, and then just a little bit farther around. But it has moved so quickly that your eye is also still seeing it in the first position.

There are hundreds of obvious examples of this persistence of vision: the spokes of a wheel cannot be seen when the wheel rotates; a striped top becomes a solid color as it spins. In comic strips, cartoonists try to indicate the existence of this illusion by drawing blurry, trailing lines behind a swiftly moving car or airplane.

Another example of persistence of vision in practical use is the way movement is achieved in motion pictures.

Look at this sketch of a strip of movie film. You will notice that each picture is a little different from the one just above it. A man is walking, and in each picture his foot is a little farther ahead than in the preceding picture.

When a movie is shown in a theater, this strip of film moves past a strong light, in little jerks. Each jerk moves it just enough to bring the next picture in front of the light, which shines through it. The film, dark in some parts, more transparent in others, according to whatever picture is on it, carves a recognizable shadow picture out of the beam of light. It makes it into a pictorial pattern of shadows. This shadow picture goes out of the projecting machine, "riding" through the air in the beam of light. It lands on the large white screen at the end of the theater, where you see it.

The first picture remains on the screen for a split second. Then a shutter in the projecting machine comes up in front and cuts off the beam. For another split second there is nothing on the screen—but, because of persistence of vision, your eye "remembers" the picture and you think it is still there.

While the shutter cuts off the light, the strip of film is jerked along, and the second picture is pulled into place before the beam of light. The shutter drops away, and the second picture is projected on the screen. This, as you can see in the drawing here, is just a little different from the first one.

Number two disappears and number three comes up, then four, five, six, and so on.*

Because in each succeeding picture the action is a little further advanced, and because your eye remembers the preceding picture, it all blends together in your eye, creating the illusion of actual motion.

In movies there are twenty-four different pictures a second. But should you slow up the speed of the projector to a point where there were less than about sixteen pictures a second, you would begin to notice a very decided flicker, and, as it went still slower, the flicker would become so pronounced that the illusion of motion

---

* The process is actually a bit more complicated than this, but this is the general principle on which it works.

would be lost. The eye can "remember" only just so long. Then persistence of vision will not function and the eye sees only a succession of flashing still pictures, which produces a headache instead of entertainment.

Persistence of vision is used in television the same way it is used in movies. And that is all we are going to say about it here in 1472. Now when you come to it again you will know the nature of the beast.

Sometime around 1670—two hundred years from here —we will find Sir Isaac Newton using persistence of vision to prove that white light is made up of a blend of all the colored lights of the spectrum. We will meet it again toward the end of the nineteenth century. And 470 years from here, in 1940, Peter Goldmark uses it to make color television practical.

Our next date peg goes at 1600 A.D., with the name of a gentleman mentioned before—William Gilbert.

Up until 1600 the sum total of all knowledge of electricity was pretty much confined to what the ancient Greeks had known—the mysterious properties of amber and the magnes.

William Gilbert, or Gylberde, the most distinguished man of science of Elizabethan England, is the "father" of modern electrical science, the man who threw the switch and ended a long blackout.

His principal book, which sums up most of his work, was published in London in 1600—three years before he died of the plague. This book, the result of years of research, mounted a formidable title, *De Magnete, magneticisque corporibus, et de magno magnete tellure.* Nevertheless, it went through five editions.

In addition to giving an account of his experiments, Gilbert set forth his great discovery—that the world is a huge magnet. For this reason the needle of a compass points to the north *pole*. His amazing conception of the world as a magnet laid a foundation for the development of the science of electricity and magnetism.

Dr. Gilbert started the ball rolling. . . .

CHAPTER FOUR

The Jumping Frog of Bologna

THE opening of the seventeenth century was a turning point in electrical science. It was also the beginning of a new era in all methods of communication.

At the turn of the century the horse still provided the best way to get around on land. On sea the English navy, fresh from its triumph over the Spanish Armada, rode on the free but variable power of the wind. Man traveled in the same way he had for thousands of years. Not that there had been no improvements—there had. But the horse and the sail remained the prime movers.

Yet the first rumblings of the approaching era of speed could be heard. The year after Dr. Gilbert published his *De Magnete* something happened down in Italy. Perhaps it did not seem very important at the time. Looking back now we realize that in 1601 Signor Giovanni Battista della Porta made the first improvement in the steam engine since Hero of Alexandria. Della Porta also invented a gadget to spray water out of fountains, the forerunner of the first completely successful steam engine, to be patented ninety-seven years later by an Englishman named Thomas Savery.

Most of us have read about alchemists at one time or another. Often we have thought of them only as characters in Elizabethan dramas. Alchemists, however, appear in the story of television, because of their interest in "phospors."

"Phospors" was the old name given to a substance which gave off a pale light without burning—like the luminous dials of watches and clocks. This phenomenon had been noticed before the present point in our story, to be sure. Pliny mentioned certain gems that gave off a light of their own. Albertus Magnus (Albert, of Cologne, scholastic philosopher of Swabia, 1206-1280) knew that diamonds become phosphorescent when heated to a certain temperature.

The first discovery of phosphorescence to produce results was made by one Vincenzo Cascariolo, cobbler of Bologna, Italy, sometime around 1603. For the next 283 years, alchemists all over the world were trying to concoct better "phosphors." (Phosphors were marvelous for magic tricks.)

They stewed them up by crude, malodorous methods, such as broiling oyster shells and sulphur. That mixture produced a feeble violet light. The only drawback was that it decomposed in moist air and smelled exactly like very rotten eggs. It was not until 1886 that a gentleman named Sidot prepared the first efficient—and non-smelling—phosphorescent substance. When television appears, we shall find what seems like "phosphorescent" paint used to make the fluorescent "screen" on which we see television.

Around the middle of the seventeenth century,

the English navy contributed a signal flag system which was a decided improvement in naval communications. Of the nautical signal systems still in use it is the oldest, and improved forms of it are used all over the world today.

And here at the middle of the century we find an old word with a new significance. It is "vacuum"—meaning a space from which everything, including air, has been removed. In the twentieth century, this word will become linked with radio and television—by the name "vacuum tube." The first air pump with which to make a vacuum was invented in 1650.

In 1663, the inventor of the air pump, Otto von Guericke, of Magdeburg, Prussian Saxony, built the first primitive machine to generate frictional or static electricity.

In 1666, Sir Isaac Newton made his classical investigation of the *spectrum*—the band of colors formed when white light shines through a glass prism. Newton's experiments led to acceptance of the fact that *all the colors of the rainbow are present in pure white light,* such as sunlight. The prism did not manufacture colors. It divided white light into the separate colors. If these separate colors were all shown on one spot at the same time, white light was again created. This principle was to be used in color television in 1940.

In 1676 Ole Roemer discovered that light travels at a definite, fixed speed.

Stimulated by the Renaissance, European scientists (principally Italian) had begun to study light during the sixteenth century. The first part of the seventeenth century witnessed great progress in the use of lenses, particularly in telescopes, microscopes, and spectacles— picking up where Friar Bacon left off. A great Dutch scientist, Christian Huygens, was writing a book called *Traité de la Lumière*.

Huygens formulated the theory that light, like sound, is a form of wave motion. In order for a wave to move, it must have something to move in. Just as a waterwave must have an ocean or lake in which to exist, so a light- wave must have something in which to wave. It couldn't be air, because light goes right through a vacuum and through the great empty spaces between planets and stars, where there is no air.

But if it was not air, then what was it? Huygens did not know, but he was sure some medium must exist— unknown, unseen. For want of a better name, he called this unknown something "ether." The name is still used today, and it still is almost as unknown.*

The last of the seventeenth century had ticked away, and the eighteenth was eight years gone, when a certain Dr. Wall had an idea. The doctor used to puzzle over the way a piece of warm amber would spark and make a crackling sound when rubbed. He wondered if this spark and the crackling noise were not the same as lightning and thunder, only in miniature. Dr. Wall got the idea, but he left it for Benjamin Franklin to prove half a century later.

If you have a television or radio set handy, look inside it. As you do so, turn the tuning dial on the front of the

* Although the name "ether" remains, Huygens' theory was disproved in 1873, as we shall see.

set and see what moves inside. You will see two or more sets of thin metal plates move in and out of each other—like a pack of cards being shuffled by unseen hands. By changing the position of one set of metal plates in relation to the other set, you "tune" in different radio stations. This gadget is called a *condenser*.

When we get to the television camera itself, we shall find that the heart of it is really a group of hundreds of thousands of tiny condensers built into one unit.

Its great-great grandfather was born in 1745—in two different places, and almost simultaneously. (That, you must admit, is a birth which fits in with television's power of enabling you to be in two places at one time.)

The ancestor of the modern condenser was the "Leyden jar," an example of which can be found in most every high school or college physics laboratory. It was first invented by E. G. von Kleist, of Kammin in the Prussian province of Pomerania.

The second inventors, a year later, were Cunaeus and Pieter van Musschenbroek, of the University of Leyden in the city of Leiden, Holland. Hence the name, Leyden jar.

The Leyden jar was able to *store up a charge of electricity*—enough to enable Sir William Watson, of England, to send an electric charge from a Leyden jar through a metal wire two miles long.

What was most important, Sir William observed that electricity *appeared* to be transmitted instantaneously. Actually, it was not instantaneous, but the speed was so great it seemed instantaneous. In later generations, men learned that both light and electricity travel through the air at the same speed—186,000 miles per second. And still later they found both light and electricity to be part of the same thing.

In June, 1752, Benjamin Franklin proved what Dr. Wall had suggested—lightning, and the spark from amber (or from the Leyden jar) are similar. The story of this scientific milestone is a familiar one, the famous experiment of the kite in the thunderstorm.

The kite was tied to one end of a piece of twine, the other end was in Franklin's hand. After the rain had thoroughly soaked the twine, it was able to conduct electricity. Franklin could draw enough electricity from the highly charged thunder clouds, down through the wet string, to put a charge into a Leyden jar. Thus "canned," the electricity was used for several experiments.

While scientists were learning more and more about electricity, the non-electric methods of communication were not standing still.

One momentous day in 1763, an unknown instrument maker of Glasgow, Scotland, was engaged by Glasgow University to repair a model of an early steam engine. The instrument maker was disturbed by the inefficiency and wastefulness of this primitive device. He set to work to improve on it. Six years later, in 1769, he took out patents on a new engine, his own invention. Thus began the rapid development of the steam engine, making possible the locomotives and ocean liners of today. The unknown Scotch instrument maker's name was James Watt.

That same year the predecessor of the automobile appeared in France. It was a steam carriage, invented by Nicholas Joseph Cugnot.

The first steamboat began to sail the waters of the Forth and Clyde Canal in 1802. It was William Symington's tug, the *Charlotte Dundas*—ancestor, by five years, of Robert Fulton's Hudson River steamboat, the *Clermont*.

In 1804, a steam train spluttered and puffed its way along the rails of a horse tramway in Wales.

Photography was having its beginning, too. In 1777, Karl Wilhelm Scheele was investigating the darkening action of sunlight on silver chloride.

The two Montgolfier brothers kindled a fire under the opening of the large linen balloon they had made, in 1783. As hot air and smoke filled the balloon, it stirred from the ground and soared slowly, steadily, into the air, for the first successful balloon ascension.

In another part of France, Claude and Ignace Chappe were attending school. They lived in two different buildings and in this school pupils in one house were not allowed to communicate with those in the other. A silly rule, thought the two brothers, so they decided to abolish it as of 1784.

They constructed a signal apparatus to send messages to each other, from building to building. It consisted of an upright pole with a cross piece nailed to the top. At each end of the cross piece was a movable wooden arm, attached by a hinge. The two arms could be set in varying positions to spell out messages according to a code the brothers had devised. Using two of these signal machines, Claude and Ignace Chappe proceeded to com-

municate with each other, in very much the way Boy
Scouts send messages with the semaphore signal flags
today.

After Claude left school, he kept improving the signal
system until, in 1792, it was adopted by the French
government.

Signal towers were built on hilltops across the coun-
tryside. A signal man in one town could just see the
towers in the two neighboring towns on either side of
him. A message started at one end of the line could be
sent a distance of 50 leagues (about 120 miles) in fifteen
minutes. The system was widely used throughout France
until the advent of the familiar dot-dash electric telegraph. Offsprings of the Chappe telegraph are seen
today in the semaphore signal still used on some railroads.

In 1791, at Bologna, Italy, a treatise was published on
the theory of animal electricity. It was the work of a
learned Italian physiologist, Luigi Galvani.

One day he had been dissecting frogs. He had just
cut a leg from a thoroughly deceased specimen and was
puzzled to find that this leg twitched violently when it
was touched by a metal knife. The knife had been lying
next to an electrical machine.

This prompted Galvani to begin his study of electricity and its relation to the functions of the body.

Galvani's discoveries of the part electricity plays in
the running of the body are one of the foundation
stones of modern scientific knowledge. His name is per-
petuated by the term "galvanism" and the "galva-
nometer"—an instrument for detecting or measuring
electric currents.

A successor of Galvani's was Alessandro Volta. He, too, pondered on the frog's leg. It would jump and twitch when touched by the knife which had lain next to an electrical machine. It would also jump when touched on a nerve by a piece of iron and simultaneously touched on a muscle by a piece of copper. Volta found that when two different kinds of metal, such as iron and copper, are joined in a circuit, a small current of electricity begins to flow from one to the other.

It was not any special feature of the frog's leg which caused it to twitch. When it was touched by the two metals, and the current passed through the nerve and muscle, the leg jumped.

In a similar way, if you happen to get an electric shock from a lighting fixture, your hand automatically jumps away without your thinking about it.

Volta's discovery pointed the way for future scientists, who learned that the communications system of the human body, the nerves, operates by the building up and discharge of tiny electro-chemical currents. These currents pass through the nerves, which serve as the telephone wires of our bodies.

Volta's discovery led also to the invention of the famous "Voltaic pile," forerunner of the modern electric storage battery.

Today Alessandro Volta's name has become a household word. From it comes the electrical term "volt"— the unit of electromotive force, the "pressure" of electricity.

So much for the jumping frog of Bologna, and so much for the eighteenth century.

CHAPTER FIVE

Moon Metal

NOWADAYS, most of us are familiar with the words "ultraviolet rays" and "infrared rays." Sun bathing, health lamps, and vitamin advertisements have made them commonplace—nearly a century and a half after their discovery. The nineteenth century began with the awareness of their existence being announced to the world. Flashing right along with them was the world's first and brightest electric light—the carbon arc, still used today in certain kinds of spotlights, movie projectors, and sun-ray lamps.

Light from the sun made the first photograph in 1802. Thomas Wedgewood cast shadows on chemically treated paper and made crude silhouette pictures.

In 1816, a Swedish scientist isolated a new "element" called selenium. Baron Jöns Jakob Berzelius, chemist, of Väfversunda Sortard, near Linköping, Sweden, discovered what grew to be the eyes of television.

He named this chemical element *selenium* after the Greek word for the moon, because it resembled another element called "tellurium," meaning "the earth" in Latin! You see, there is a touch of fantasy in science, behind the scenes. When scientists began to use it for experiments, it would have sounded altogether too frivolous for one professor to ask another for a soupçon of "moon" metal. Too much like letting down one's hair in public. So, with all etymological precision, it was called selenium.

Three years after Berzelius put the finger on selenium in Sweden, something significant happened in a neighboring Scandinavian country. Across the waters of the Skagerrak, in Denmark, lived an electrical researcher named Hans Christian Oersted.

Mr. Oersted had been trying to figure out why the needle of his mariner's compass always moved when he put it near an electric wire. By 1819, he reached this conclusion:

When an electric current runs through a wire, it automatically creates a field of magnetic force all around the wire. It was that magnetism which made the needle of the compass move.

If Mr. Oersted had not spotted it, we might have had to wait much longer for television, radio, electric light, telephones, movies, or electric razors. But he did. This one observation pointed the way for a certain Michael Faraday, who, in turn, opened up the science of modern electricity.

As we have come up through the centuries, we have looked at a number of seemingly unrelated things. For instance, the discovery of selenium, the first photograph, and the work of Mr. Oersted do not seem to have anything in common. Perhaps it all seems like a lot of loose ends. Actually, we shall find that everything ties together to produce television. Thousands and thousands of different discoveries contributed to the great total sum of knowledge, by which men have learned to see at a distance.

As a matter of fact, a great deal of interesting material has been left out of this story—simply because there is not room for it. We would need about three or four thousand pages to cover everything with any degree of thoroughness.

That being the case, let us concentrate only on the most important facts, the stories most necessary for a rounded understanding of what modern television is and how it works. By sticking to this we will avoid getting tangled up in history and technicalities.

The year following Oersted's discovery, two different scientists each discovered that electricity has the power to magnetize iron and steel. Going on from there, a third scientist, W. Sturgeon, bent a soft iron bar into the shape of a horseshoe. He wound some insulated wire around the horseshoe, connected the wire to a "voltaic pile," or battery, and ran a current through it. As long as the current was passing through the wire, it changed the iron bar into a powerful magnet.

This was the first *electro-magnet*. The electro-magnet became the heart of the loudspeaker used in your television or radio set.

The word *microphone* appears about this time, too. Sir Charles Wheatstone coined the term "micro-phone" to describe an acoustic gadget he had built for magnifying small sounds.*

* Although the word is the same, it was not a microphone as we know it today.

Now we come to an important date peg—1831—with a most important name, Michael Faraday.

Michael Faraday was a distinguished man of science in the England of Victoria with many friends in Parliament. One particular politician friend, named Gladstone, considered himself a far-seeing, practical realist, in the interests of his constituents, et cetera and so forth!

When he learned that Faraday was spending considerable sums of good English money in experiments on a contraption called an electro-magnet, the practical-realist side of him came to the fore. He observed that, instead of throwing money away on a toy, it would be better to give it to a worthy charity—to assist the needy and impoverished.

Counter-observed Mr. Faraday, "Someday, sir, you may be able to tax it and that will give you revenue for the poor."

This little toy wound up as the dynamo, and, by 1866 or 1867, dynamos were being sold for the production of electricity.

You see, Michael Faraday was a man who started something. For instance, in 1831 he announced to the world the laws of "electro-magnetic induction."*

Oersted had found that an electric wire was surrounded by invisible magnet attraction. Faraday picked up from there.

Perhaps we should say a little bit about this invisible magnetic "attraction." First we found it in the Magnes stone, in 800 B.C. Now it pops up around a wire carrying electricity. You can't see it, smell it, hear it, or feel

---

* Joseph Henry, in America, also discovered the principles of induction at just about the same time.

it. But you can see and feel its *effect* on a certain object. There is a simple trick, done by most students, to see the effect of these *invisible lines of magnetic force*. You need one magnet, a piece of paper, and an ounce or two of iron filings.

Place the magnet on a table, and lay the sheet of paper over it. Prop up the edges of the paper with some magazines, or anything that will keep it level. Now, pour

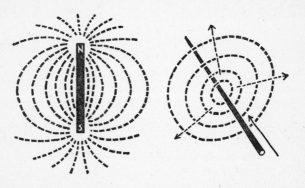

some of the iron filings on top of the paper, right over the magnet. Tap the paper gently, and the iron filings will arrange themselves in a pattern of lines which radiate out from each end of the magnet, just as in this drawing.

The explanation of this "magic" trick is simple: *invisible lines of magnetic force* radiate out from the magnet. Iron is attracted by them, and the loose iron filings are pulled into positions corresponding to those of the lines of force.

The same kind of lines surround a wire carrying electricity, except they surround it in circles, as shown in this sketch.

When a current starts to run through a wire, they jump out into position. When the current stops, they are "sucked" back again, or collapse back to the wire.

In "alternating current," such as we use in most homes today, the current runs first in one direction, then it stops and runs in the other direction. Every time it changes its direction, the old set of magnetic lines of force is sucked back into the wire, and a new set jumps out.

If you want to take another look at the last two drawings, it might help. If you get some idea of how magnetic lines of force might look, you will find it a useful bit of knowledge. It is very important for television, and it will explain a lot of the "magic" of television later on.

On August 29, 1831, Faraday first realized he might be able to produce a current in one wire by means of a current in another, separate, wire. Four weeks later he wrote to a friend, "I am busy just now again on electromagnetism, and I think I have got hold of a good thing, but can't say. It may be a weed instead of a fish that, after all my labour, I may at last pull up."

He caught no weed but a most excellent fish!

Briefly, this is what he found:

If you have two wires running side by side, close together, and a current passes through one of them, the lines of magnetism spread out from that wire and hit the other. When they hit the second wire an electric current is created, *induced* in the second wire. The new current is exactly like the one in the first wire, and it runs in the same direction.

If you reverse the current in the first wire, the lines of

force are "sucked" back. As they come back, they hit the second wire again. This causes the second current to change its direction, too.

Every time the current in the first wire changes its direction, the current it induces in the second wire also alternates.

At this point, someone is bound to be asking, "Why?" To tell you the honest truth, nobody really knows, any more than we know what makes life and death. It just happens—it is a phenomenon, a most important phenomenon.

Michael Faraday also found out that he could create, or *generate*, an electric current merely by moving a wire past a magnet, so that it broke through the "invisible lines of magnetic force." If he passed one wire by the magnet, he generated one current. If he passed a group of ten wires by the magnet, he generated a current in *each* wire—or a total of ten electrical impulses. And each time the wires passed by the magnet, cutting through the lines of magnetic force, a new set of electric impulses was generated.

Perhaps now you have begun to suspect why we are paying so much attention to Mr. Faraday's experiments. Of course! From it was created the dynamo. Possibly you have guessed how a dynamo works.

Essentially, it is a bunch of wires, thousands and thousands of them, spinning past one magnet after another. In so doing, the wires cut through lines of magnetism and thereby generate a steady flow of electrical impulses.

Putting together what Oersted, Sturgeon, and Faraday discovered, we get:

(1) An electric current moving in a wire will magnetize a piece of iron next to it, forming an *electromagnet.*

(2) *The magnetic field built up by a current flowing in one wire will generate a current in another wire close to it.* This is called *electro-magnetic induction.*

(3) *If a wire breaks through the lines of force of a magnet, a current is generated in that wire.*

These discoveries in electro-magnetism tie together two of the main threads of our story: the thread of magnetism started in 800 B.C. in ancient Greece, with the magical Magnes stone. The thread of electricity started in 640 B.C., with the strange power of the Elektron stone.

Where does it lead? Not only to the dynamo, which was the first practical development, but also to nearly every modern electrical device, and—what concerns us most in this story—to the microphone, the television camera, and the transmitter, which sends the sound and pictures through the air, and to the receiver with its picture screen and loudspeaker.

There remains a third main thread of our story.

CHAPTER SIX

The Blink of the Eye

PROGRESS was the order of the nineteenth century.

1832—Schilling was building a telegraph system in Europe. Samuel F. B. Morse was working on one in the United States. By 1836, the electric telegraph was beginning to come into use.

1839—The first successful methods of photography were invented, three in one year.

On January 5, Fox Talbot described his method to the Royal Society, in England. He called it a *photogenic* drawing.

February 6, across the channel in France, an announcement was made of the "Daguerreotype." The inventors are three: Nicéphore de Niepce, his nephew Isidore, and Louis Jacques Mandé Daguerre.

Later that year in England, Sir John F. W. Herschel invented another method, coined the photographic terms, "positive" and "negative," and learned how to "fix" a plate (picture) so exposure to additional light would not ruin it.

In 1839, Edmond Becquerel made his observations of

the electro-chemical effect of light—pointing towards the discovery of photo-electric cells.

Sir John Herschel also paved the way for the discovery of fluorescence, by Sir George Stokes, in 1852. Fluorescence was destined to find a place in television. In the late 1930's the screen on which television pictures appeared would be covered with fluorescent paint.

In 1842, English physicist Alexander Bain had a method of *facsimile,* for sending still pictures. His method formed the basis of modern facsimile methods for sending photographs.

Michael Faraday began his second great period of research in 1845 and discovered the effect of magnetism on polarized light. In television cameras and receivers of the 1940's, the formation of pictures will often be controlled by magnetism.

In 1846, a Vermonter, Royal E. House, patented the first teletype system. An operator could type a message on a keyboard, and it would be automatically typed out at the other end of the circuit.

1847 brought a "copying telegraph," invented by Bakewell, and employing a method which we now call "scanning"—a word to remember. And on February 11, 1847, Thomas Alva Edison was born in Milan, Ohio.

Color photography came the following year when Edmond Becquerel reproduced the colors of the spectrum on a daguerreotype plate.

As early as 1842, New Jerseyite Joseph Henry had reasoned that the electric discharge from a Leyden jar might be "oscillatory"—that is, a current which alternated very rapidly. Shortly after the middle of the century, Lord Kelvin proved this to be true. (That led, in another four decades, to the discovery of radio waves by Heinrich Hertz.)

The first actual transmission of a picture by electricity came in the early part of 1862. The Abbé Caselli sent a drawing through a wire from Amiens to Paris.

At this time, the electric telegraph was growing, improving, and spreading across the land. Its next logical step was to spread across the sea, and in 1845 a submarine cable spanned the English channel.

Engineers cocked an eye at the Atlantic Ocean and set to work, laying a transatlantic cable. Dogged by failure in several attempts, it was not until 1866 that their job was done. On August 16 of that year, an exchange of greetings between Queen Victoria and President Buchanan formally opened the first transatlantic telegraph.

In 1873, a great mathematician, James Clerk Maxwell, published a great book in which he reorganized Faraday's ideas and set them down in precise, mathematical form.

And what was most important, Maxwell declared that *light is really a form of electro-magnetic wave*. He figured it out by mathematics! His theory was not proved by actual experiment until Heinrich Hertz did his experiments more than a decade later.

Maxwell's treatise was the big event of 1873. But there were two other significant happenings—one in Austria and one in Ireland.

In Vienna, a certain type of dynamo was in use. It was called a Gramme dynamo. Viennese engineers found that if you took the current from one dynamo and ran it into another, it moved. It turned the second dynamo into a motor. This was how the electric motor was discovered—in 1873. Eight years later, electric trolley cars were on display in Paris.

The third big event of the year started as trouble in the transatlantic cable station, at Valentia, Ireland. A cable operator named May first noticed that a stick of crystalline selenium, used as a "resister" in a circuit, offered less resistance to an electric current when exposed to light than when in the dark. It was the same selenium Berzelius had discovered in 1816. He reported this fact to his superior, Mr. Willoughby Smith, who investigated the matter further and then wrote a letter to the Vice-President of the Society of Telegraph Engineers, of which he was a member. At the Twelfth Ordinary General Meeting of the Society, on February 12, 1873, the Vice-President read this letter to the group:

> Wharf Road
> 4th February, 1873
>
> My dear Latimer Clark,
>
> Being desirous of obtaining a more suitable high resistance for use at the shore station in connection with my system of testing and signaling during the submersion of long submarine cables, I was induced to experiment with bars of selenium.
>
> The early experiments did not place selenium in a very favorable light . . . there was a great discrepancy in the tests, and seldom did different operators obtain the same result. While investigating the cause of such great differences in the resistances of bars, it was found that the resistance altered materially according to the intensity of light to which they were subjected. When the bars were fixed in a box with a sliding cover, so as to exclude all light, their resistance was at its highest, and remained very constant . . . but immediately the cover of the box was removed, the conductivity increased from 15 to 100 per cent. . . .

. . . If . . . you think this communication of sufficient
interest, perhaps you will bring it before the meeting. . . .

I remain, yours faithfully,
Willoughby Smith

Selenium was *photo-electric*. These observations by
Smith, and his assistant, May, were corroborated by the
Earl of Rosse and other scientists, who proved the erratic
behavior of selenium was due solely to light.

The realization of selenium's photo-electric quality led
to the first television methods. In fact, May seems to
have recognized the possibilities and built a machine to
transmit pictures electrically. Apparently the machine
did not work, but at least the "eye" of television blinked.
The first recognized television system appeared two years
later—in 1875—which is in the next chapter.

CHAPTER SEVEN

Television—Model 1875

TELEVISION in 1875, indeed!

No, it is not a joke.

It was about 1875 when an American, G. R. Carey, of Boston, designed what was probably the first television system.

He tried to imitate the human eye, to view a picture

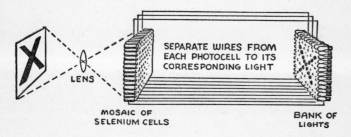

SEPARATE WIRES FROM
EACH PHOTOCELL TO ITS
CORRESPONDING LIGHT

LENS

MOSAIC OF
SELENIUM CELLS

BANK OF
LIGHTS

and send all of it in one gulp—mechanically difficult, to say the least. It was a bit beyond the capabilities of Mr. Carey's gadget.

Nevertheless, if you look at the diagram of his idea, you must admit it was clever.

The design is focused on the "retina" by a lens, just as in the human eye.

You remember, in the Prologue, the retina was studded with "nerve endings" which are *photo-electric*, and give off an electric impulse when touched by light.

In place of the nerve endings, Carey substituted a *mosaic* of selenium cells, which would react to light in a photo-electric manner.

Each cell is connected by a separate wire to an electric light. There are just as many lights as cells. Each light, in the bank of lamps, occupies the same corresponding position as its selenium cell in the mosaic.

The design of light, focused on the mosaic, touches some of the cells, causing them to react and pass a current. The other cells, untouched by light, do not react and therefore pass no current.

The cells which do react send currents through their wires to their electric lamps. The lamps light up—reproducing the shape of the original design.

Very little detail can be sent by such a crude method—only rough outline. A detailed picture would require at least a quarter of a million cells, wires, and lamps. Obviously, it would be too cumbersome.

Carey had improved on May's idea—for May had focused his picture on one single selenium cell and expected it to transmit the entire picture. Carey divided the picture into sections, he *dissected* it, and tried to send all of the sections, simultaneously, through a number of separate wires. He failed because selenium cells alone could not drive currents through wires to the bank of lamps. The tiny currents of the cells were too weak. They would have to be magnified (*amplified*) millions of times before they would be strong enough. *Amplifier* radio tubes capable of performing such a task had not been invented. The man who was going to invent the radio tube, Lee de Forest, was not quite ready for the job, being only two years old at the time.

Carey made his big contribution to television when he divided the picture into sections before trying to transmit it. This principle has remained fundamental in all television systems. Scientists continued to experiment with his idea, and thirty-one years later, in 1906, two Frenchmen—Fournier and Rignoux—were able to get their own version of Carey's idea to transmit a crude outline through a wire.

Carey's idea was not the answer to the riddle, but it did have grandchildren. The electric news bulletin board encompassing the Times Building in Times Square, New York City, is a descendant. So was the huge electric sign with the animated cartoon advertisement a few blocks farther uptown.

In 1875, an English scientist, Dr. John Kerr, discovered what later became known as the "Kerr Effect." From it was developed the "Kerr Cell," a device used to control light rays in a number of mechanical television systems of later years.

In 1876, Alexander Graham Bell patented the telephone, and Elisha Gray and Thomas Edison patented similar ideas for transmitting speech. Edison also "invented" the phonograph in 1876. Over in Paris, a visiting Russian officer, Paul Jablochkov, perfected the "electric candle"—a development of the carbon arc light. It introduced the era of electric street lighting. In London, David Hughes was inventing the first real microphone, as we know it today.

In 1878, the first *cathode rays* were generated by Sir William Crookes, beginning the development of the cathode ray tube—on which television of the 1930's and 1940's would be based.

In 1879, Edison made his first incandescent electric light bulb, putting electric light into the home.

Under the stimulus of all these inventions, a number of ideas were brought forward for transmitting pictures electrically.

One of these early methods was briefly described by two English scientists, Ayrton and Perry, in a letter to *Nature* magazine, dated April 21, 1880. They had heard that Alexander Graham Bell had, as they thought, discovered a method for seeing by electric telegraphy. Ayrton and Perry apparently feared Bell might gain a monopoly on telegraphic vision, and they pointed out that a number of English scientists had been discussing methods of seeing by telegraph ever since 1873. They described their own system, similar to Carey's method (of which they probably had not heard, since it was not listed at the U. S. Patent Office). Their idea had been suggested by a picture in *Punch* magazine, in 1877, and was governed by Willoughby Smith's experiments. They stressed that the idea of "seeing by telegraph" belonged jointly to a number of men, not to any single person, saying, "The discovery of the light effect of selenium carries with it the principle of a plan for seeing by electricity."

Actually, as it turned out, Graham Bell had not found a system for seeing by electricity, but rather a most ingenious method of transmitting sound on a beam of light.

But, other television systems were designed around this time by Sawyer, Senlecq, de Païva, and Leblanc.

The idea brought forward by the French scientist, Maurice Leblanc, late in 1880, picked up where the other methods of "dissecting" the picture had left off. Carey, for instance, separated the picture into small bits which were to be transmitted simultaneously. Leblanc suggested an ingenious theory of *scanning*—and when we examine a modern television camera, we shall see how important it was.

Briefly, Leblanc's idea was this: Instead of trying to transmit an entire picture, all in one indigestible gulp, take it in nibbles. Break the picture up into tiny spots—varying shades of light and dark. Separate it into uniform size bits, like the tiles in a bathroom floor. Then send these little pieces, one after another, in definite, precise order. As the pieces arrive at their destination, reassemble them in the same order—like a jigsaw puzzle.

This idea of breaking a picture into little bits is important, because it is the only practical way yet found to reproduce a picture rapidly.

It is used not only in television, but also in printing. Look at any illustration in a newspaper. Hold it very close, and it is a meaningless series of black and white spots. But go back a few feet from it and see what happens. It turns into a recognizable picture.

The most important figure in electrical science in ~~the~~ Europe of the 1880's was Heinrich Rudolf Hertz. Hertz set out to prove Maxwell was right—in declaring *light to be an electro-magnetic wave.*

While he was busy proving this, he discovered how

to make radio waves and send them through space. In his day, they were called "Hertzian Waves."

Hertz proved that *radio waves are electro-magnetic,* and travel through space at the speed of light—186,000 miles a second. He could produce them by sparking a Leyden jar, or even by scuffing his leather shoes across a carpet on a cold day.

Next, Hertz accidentally discovered what is called the "photo-electric" effect—the effect of light on electricity.

While he was experimenting with his newly discovered electric (radio) waves, he hit trouble. In his apparatus were two electric wires separated by only a small space. Every so often, sparks would begin to jump across the gap, from one wire to the other.

Hertz tracked down the cause of this sparking—a piece of magnesium he was burning. The brilliant, intense light from the burning magnesium hit the metal wires and knocked a stream of electrical energy—sparks, or a stream of *electrons*, as was later discovered—from one wire to the other.*

Having found the cause, Hertz was not long in finding that radio waves could be reflected (like light in a mirror), and refracted, or bent, as light is when it goes through a prism or through water.

On the morning of August 25, 1940, the following

* In 1874, an Englishman, G. Johnstone Stoney, had announced the discovery of the "tiniest natural unit of electricity." In 1891, four years after Hertz discovered the "photo-electric" effect, Stoney named his "tiniest unit" the *electron*. Exactly what are electrons? Briefly, they are "point charges" of negative electricity. They are nearly 2000 times smaller than hydrogen atoms, which are the smallest atoms there are—too small to be seen in the most powerful microscope. And that is pretty small.

story appeared in the *New York Times*—tucked away in the middle of the obituary columns:

Berlin, Aug. 24—Dr. Paul Nipkow, a pioneer in the field of television, died here this morning. He had celebrated his eightieth birthday on Thursday and on that occasion he slipped and fell, apparently fracturing his thigh. In order to determine the extent of his injuries he was taken to a hospital, where he died of a heart attack this morning.

Berlin, Aug. 24 (AP)—In 1884 Dr. Nipkow patented an invention known as "the electrical telescope," but his patent lapsed when he was unable to pay the costs of extending it. For the next thirty-two years he worked as an engineer for a railway signal company. In the meantime his idea was developed and improved by others.

Six years ago Dr. Nipkow finally received public recognition when he was selected honorary president of the newly-founded German Television Society.

The "Nipkow disk," which Dr. Nipkow invented in 1884, played an indispensable part in the production of television until a few years ago. Lately it has been superseded by other devices.

One small article marked the passing of Paul Nipkow, whose only "public" recognition had been an appointment to a society run for Nazi propaganda purposes.

Paul Nipkow recognized the limitations of Carey's method and the importance of the theory of scanning. Instead of trying to use countless wires, cells, and lamps—as Carey had done—he invented, in 1884, the "Nipkow disk"—a revolving metal disk, perforated with a series of holes. This is used to *scan* the picture and separate it into tiny sections.

Nipkow's "scanning disk"—is most ingenious, but an understanding of how it works is not vital to our story.*

Suffice it to say Nipkow's disk formed the basis of most television methods until the early 1930's. By that time the limitations of its principle were so apparent, it was abandoned in favor of the cathode ray tube method.

In Nipkow's time, though, it was a prodigious step forward. Unfortunately, he lacked an efficient and quick-acting electric eye to record the varying light waves. Selenium cells were too sluggish, and Nipkow never was able to put his invention into use.

Another reason for Nipkow's inability to make his system practical was the lack of a reliable and efficient method to amplify, to increase, the power of the tiny electric currents created by the selenium electric eye. This lack was to be remedied by Lee de Forest in 1906.

Television from 1884 up through 1932 was also limited by the physical inability of any revolving disk to move fast enough. Television demanded more speed than mechanical wheels could supply. Only electrons were fast enough—and they had to be harnessed. The human eye did it. Human ingenuity was going to do it.

The science of electronics was developing—not with the speed of light, perhaps—but developing nonetheless. The era of electricity was beginning. In fact, on June 4, 1888, electrocution became the officially favored way of executing criminals in New York. Shocking, but electronic!

---

* Detailed explanations are available in nearly every television book and encyclopedia.

It is also time to get the movies started. The remarkable Tom Edison, having "invented" the phonograph in 1876, wanted to supplement it with a picture machine. So, he "invented" movies the next year. By 1889 he had his first pieces of Eastman-Kodak film, and made his first movie in his West Orange, New Jersey, laboratory. The film showed a man sneezing. Thus was Hollywood conceived!

While Edison was starting the movie industry, a new type of mechanical scanning system of television was designed in Europe. L. Weiller proposed to replace the Nipkow disk with a rotating drum, studded with tiny mirrors. Each mirror was placed at a slightly different angle, and when the drum revolved it would scan all parts of the picture and reflect the light rays on to a selenium cell. In later years, the mirror drum was greatly improved by a number of different engineers, and often used in early television apparatus.

Actually, Weiller was not the first one to design a mirror drum. An Englishman, L. B. Atkinson, made an electrical seeing apparatus using a drum in 1882, but no description of it was ever published, and Weiller is usually considered the inventor, *circa* 1889.

In 1892, Professor Edouard Branly, of Paris, built a device to detect Hertzian, or radio, waves. Another pioneer, Sir Oliver Lodge, improved the idea and gave it a name—the "coherer." Lodge demonstrated the "coherer" to the British Association in 1894, as part of a system for the transmission and reception of electric telegraph messages.

A certain Italian professor attended the lectures and

on returning to Italy told a young radio engineer in Bologna about the Branly-Lodge "coherer." It was of no little assistance to this young scientist, who improved it and used it in his own experiments. The young man, son of an Irish mother, Anna Jameson, and an Italian father, was Guglielmo Marconi.

At the same time, a Parisian named Demerry was blending voice and picture with his "chronophotophone" —a combination phonograph and magic lantern, which was quite successful.

In England, Sir William Preece was signaling by wireless between two places on the Bristol Channel.

In Germany, Wilhelm Konrad Roentgen was discovering "Roentgen Rays"—better known today as "X-rays."

In France of 1896, H. Becquerel found "radio-active" powers in certain minerals—and paved the way for the study of "radio-activity" by P. Curie and Madame Curie, who discovered radium.

As the nineteenth century was coming to a close, Karl Braun made his "Braun (cathode ray) tube," forerunner of the television picture receiver of the 1930's and 1940's. Braun learned, too, that electrons are attracted by magnetism and can be controlled by magnetic force. Then, by coating the inside end of his cathode ray tube with a fluorescent substance, he was able to trace the path of the electrons—just as in modern television receivers.

And pointing to the future, the steamer *R. F. Matthews* collided with the East Goodwin Sands Lightship on the 28th of April, 1899. The vessel was equipped

with wireless, and she sent out the first S O S in history.*
The stage was set for the twentieth century!

* In those days, the letters S O S were not used for the distress signal.
The letters C Q D were used. S O S came into use at a later date.

CHAPTER EIGHT

Twentieth Century—Limited

BEFORE August, 1900, there was no such word as "television." We have glibly used it in the first few thousand years of this story, but the business of seeing-at-a-distance was not baptized as such until after the present century began to tick itself away.

Before 1900, such words as "telescopy," "electrical telescope," or "telectroscopy" were used. In fact, the British patent office used the term "telescopy" until 1908.

Apparently the first person actually to coin the word "tele-vision," from Latin and Greek, was a Frenchman named Perskyi. In preparing some material listed in the "Annexes, Congrès Internationale d'Electricité," for August 18 through 25, 1900, Perskyi seems to have given birth to the French word, *télévision,* in its modern connotation.

There is another who lays claim to parenthood. In the August, 1928, issue of *Radio News,* the editor and publisher, Hugo Gernsback, wrote:

"The word 'television' was first coined by myself in an article entitled 'Television and the Telephot,' which appeared in the December, 1909, issue of *Modern Electrics*."

Thus, in one way or another, television acquired its modern name. From time to time, efforts have been made to rechristen it with such words as "radio-vision," but television has stuck and seems destined for posterity.

Towards the end of the nineteenth century, inventions such as the telephone, the Branly "coherer," and the discovery of radio waves by Hertz had made possible the wireless transmission of dot-dash telegraph signals.

The highly complicated business of sending pictures by wireless was still some years away. It was much easier to send speech, and that was the next step.

The human voice flashed through space for the first time during Christmas week, 1900. An American engineer, Reginald A. Fessenden, transmitted it over a distance of about a mile, at Cob Point, Maryland. According to the records, he reported his results as "poor in quality, but intelligible."

Wireless made a more dramatic bid for fame a few days later. On New Year's Day, 1901, a ship in distress—the bark *Medora*—wirelessed for assistance. What was most important for all concerned, the message was picked up and help arrived. It was the second time a vessel had used wireless to send out an S O S.

This was back in the days after the Spanish-American War. McKinley had just been elected to his second term as President; the Floradora girls were quite the thing; New Mexico and Arizona had not yet become states.

The Atlantic Ocean had been spanned by cable long ago. Why should it not be spanned by wireless, too?

That was the challenge which presented itself to young Guglielmo Marconi.

A ship's crew had been saved by wireless. A vessel two hundred and fifty miles distant from England had been able to pick up a message despite the curvature of the earth's surface. However, the nearest part of America was nearly two thousand miles from Europe. Would wireless go so far?

Marconi did not know, but he was going to find out.

In the early part of December, 1901, he landed at St. John's, Newfoundland, accompanied by two assistants, G. S. Kemp and P. W. Paget. They set up their equipment on Signal Hill, above the town, and went to work.

Marconi had arranged for the wireless station in Poldhu, England, to send out a signal for three hours every afternoon. The signal was simple—the letter "S" in Morse code—three dots.

The experimenters raised their aerial wire by attaching it to a balloon. The first day, December 11th, it was ripped away by the winter gales.

The second day, they used a kite. The wind seized it and carried the antenna several hundred feet up into the winter sky.

About half-past eleven Marconi began to listen. Thirty minutes passed. Nothing came through. The three men checked their equipment over and over. Everything in order.

Twelve-fifteen—nothing.

Twelve-thirty—nothing.

Then, a little click, and another, and another—dot, dot, dot. The Morse code signal for "S." It was coming through!

The three men took turns listening. Each of them heard it. Over and over the signal clicked out. It was flashing through space, from England to a kite whipping about in the sky above Newfoundland.

To make doubly sure, Marconi tried again the next day. Again he was successful. He waited still another day, and checked once more, flying the kite higher. When the signal came in the third day there could be no doubt.

On Sunday, December 15, 1901, a slightly incredulous world learned that the Atlantic Ocean was no barrier to wireless. The *New York Times* sagely commented that Marconi would be remembered in history, that his wireless might be "transforming in its effect on the social life." Six years later, the same newspaper was receiving "wireless press messages" from London.

The world was surprised by Marconi. It was just as surprised in 1903 when two brothers, Wilbur and Orville Wright, added a gasoline motor to their airplane glider and made a flight lasting 53 seconds.

Talking motion pictures had their start in 1906. Eugene Augustin Lauste, an electrical engineer working for Edison as well as for the old Biograph movie company, patented an invention of his own. He had a method of "simultaneously recording and reproducing movements and sounds." His patent is the master patent through which modern sound movies developed.

The science of electronics was due for another landmark or two of its own. In 1905, Albert Einstein announced the theory of the photo-electric effect. This theory was to become the fundamental principle of the modern television camera. It defined the way in which the camera would turn a picture into electricity.

Another big advance in electronics came in 1906—the radio tube. Back in the 1890's, an Englishman named J. Ambrose Fleming had begun to experiment with something called a "vacuum tube," or, as he later called it, a "Thermionic valve."

By 1904, Fleming had produced his first successful "two element" Thermionic valve. It could detect radio signals—replacing the Branly "coherer." Fleming's valve pointed the way to an efficient method of amplifying electric impulses millions of times.

The method came in 1906, when an American, Lee de Forest, invented the "three element" radio tube. He fashioned it out of a bit of wire and an electric lamp from a Christmas tree. If the camera is the "eye," of television, and the microphone the "ear," then the de Forest invention must be called the "heart" of radio and television, for it builds up, pumps out, the electronic bloodstream.

The next vital contribution to television came in 1907, made by a great Russian physicist, Boris Rosing, of the St. Petersburg Technological Institute. He patented a television system, using a receiver essentially the same as the modern receiving set. It was based on the Braun cathode ray tube.

As early as 1859, the effects caused by the discharge of electricity through a vacuum had been studied by the German physicist and mathematician, Julius Plücker, who coined the name "cathode ray." Plücker was also the first scientist to investigate the effect of magnetism on cathode rays. K. F. Braun perfected his cathode ray tube in 1897, and A. R. B. Wehnelt further improved it in 1904 and 1905. Then, in 1907, Rosing designed a way in which it might be used to reproduce pictures.

For the transmitter, Rosing called for an improved mechanical system—two revolving drums studded with little mirrors. Unfortunately, he never obtained satisfactory pictures, for he was held back by the imperfections of early cathode ray tubes and photo-electric cells, and by the lack of a device to *amplify* the tiny electric impulses from his photo-electric cells. Radio tubes, having only just been invented, were still in de Forest's laboratory—four and a half thousand miles away in New York.

One of Rosing's students was a young man named Vladimir Kosma Zworykin, who—twenty-six years later—was going to perfect the first satisfactory television camera, based on the cathode ray tube—a camera which changed the course of television through the world in the latter half of the 1930's.

Shortly after Willoughby Smith's observations on the photo-electric nature of selenium, early in 1873, there had been a great surge of ideas for seeing by electricity. Most of these were announced between 1875 and 1885. When it became apparent that selenium was not a magic elixir, which could turn the trick by itself, interest waned.

Another rush of television had begun around 1905, and most of the important developments of the first two decades of twentieth-century television were grouped between 1905 and 1908.

In April, 1908, M. Armegaud, President of the French

Society of Aerial Navigation, even went so far as to tell the Paris correspondent of the *London Times* that he was sure, as a consequence of the advance already made by his apparatus, that within a year "we shall be watching one another across distances hundreds of miles apart."

In June, 1908, one of the leading English scientists, Shelford Bidwell, stressed that the only feasible way to extend vision electrically over long distances was suggested by the structure of the eye. He figured that a rough mechanical equivalent of the eye—with about 90,000 cells, wires, and lights—could be made and would transmit moving pictures by wire. The only trouble was the expense. Bidwell calculated the cost for one transmitter and receiver to be around six and a quarter million dollars. By application of the three-color principle, he believed it would be possible to transmit moving pictures in natural colors, but it would multiply the cost by three. All these calculations of Shelford Bidwell were based on the construction of a *mechanical* system of transmitting and receiving pictures—using a Nipkow disk or some variation, such as a Weiller mirror drum. He believed the only way electrical seeing could be achieved was by mechanical methods.

In answer to Bidwell, another English scientist wrote a letter to the magazine *Nature*—setting down an idea of classic brilliance.

This scientist wrote that while mechanical methods were impractical, electrical seeing could be accomplished by the use of two "kathode" ray tubes, in the transmitter and the receiver. And he added:

The real difficulties lie in devising an efficient transmitter, which, under influence of light and shade, shall sufficiently vary the necessary alterations in the intensity of the kathode beam of the receiver, and further in making this transmitter sufficiently rapid in its action to respond to the 160,000 variations per second that are necessary as a minimum.

Possibly no photoelectric phenomenon at present known will provide what is required in this respect, but should something suitable be discovered, distant electric vision will, I think, come within the region of possibility.

(signed)   A. A. Campbell-Swinton.

This idea of Campbell-Swinton's was similar to Boris Rosing's, in the use of a cathode ray tube receiver, but differed in the use of a *cathode ray tube camera* as well. Undoubtedly it was first conceived independently of Rosing, for Rosing's idea had not yet been patented and published. Although Campbell-Swinton's method was only a sketchy suggestion in 1908, he worked it out in considerable detail, which he described to the Roentgen Society in November, 1911.

People take it for granted that television is completely new—something just invented in the last few years. Actually, by 1908, when Campbell-Swinton sketched out his idea, most of the fundamental points on which modern television is based were already known. When Vladimir Zworykin perfected his camera and revolutionized television in the 1930's, he was using the principles laid down by Campbell-Swinton in 1908. It is quite possible we might have had television in general use by the end of the second decade of this century— had not the First World War intervened, virtually to end the development of television for the better part of a decade. And the disintegration of western civilization which followed the first war retarded its progress again

—retarded it another decade but did not stop it completely, for television was inevitable.

After 1906, and in the years preceding the outbreak of war, Lee de Forest continued to develop his radio tube. In the spring of 1907, the United States Navy wireless operator at the Brooklyn Navy Yard was astounded to hear music coming through his earphones for the first time in history. This first musical broadcast, of a record of the *William Tell* overture, traveled the immense distance of four miles from a laboratory in Manhattan, where de Forest was hard at work with his assistant, John V. L. Hogan.

In 1941, de Forest and a friend—and several million eavesdroppers—had a chat about this event over a coast-to-coast radio program—de Forest in Los Angeles and his friend in New York.

Said de Forest, "No one could possibly have foreseen what is occurring right now between Los Angeles and New York, because then [in 1907] the amplifier, which has since made possible the transcontinental telephone, was only a crude little glass 'baby,' lying in swaddling cotton in that little old shoe box in our laboratory."

When, that spring day in 1907, de Forest and Hogan finally got their apparatus to work, they did not quite know what to do with it. Finally de Forest decided to rig up a wire from the flagpole on top of their building and send out signals—using a recording of the overture to *William Tell*.

De Forest put it this way. "Maybe we can get our signals out a little way. Perhaps someone will hear us.

We won't try to reach anyone in particular. We'll just let 'er go free. We'll *broadcast* it."

That was just what they did, and made history by startling the wireless operator at the Brooklyn Navy Yard, when he heard music instead of the usual dot-dash code.

That also appears to have been the origin of the word *broadcast*, used in its modern sense.

The young man who operated the transmitter at this epochal broadcast, John Vincent Lawless Hogan, became one of America's foremost radio engineers and inventors. Among the more familiar of his inventions was a blessing he bestowed on radio audiences everywhere—single dial tuning. In early radio sets it was necessary to twiddle around with three or four or more knobs and dials to tune in a station. Hogan invented the device which made it possible for you to tune your radio with one single motion of your hand. In addition to a number of other television and radio inventions, he developed the rectifier heterodyne, and one of the best systems of *facsimile*, the "radio printing press," used to send still pictures and printed material by radio.

And, a quarter of a century after that first musical broadcast, he was experimenting with television at his New York laboratory. To provide sound accompaniment for the radio-pictures, he played recordings of music by Bach, Beethoven, and Brahms. Hogan's sound transmitter operated on the frequency of 1550 kilocycles, right next to the standard broadcast band—which in the mid-1930's ended at 1500 kilocycles. Radio listeners, who fiddled about with their sets, began to pick up the music from Hogan's sound transmitter. Although they were unable to see the pictures, they enjoyed the recorded classics at a time when little good music was broadcasted on American radio. They wrote letters, asking for more music, and still more.

To accommodate this unexpected audience, Mr. Hogan set up radio station W2XR, dedicated to the transmission of good musical programs. In 1937, the name was changed to WQXR. Its policy of good taste and good music brought a peaceful revolution in the quality of American broadcasting, and a notable contribution to American culture.

In 1907, de Forest's tube was used only as a "detector" to catch radio waves. No one dreamed it could be made to "oscillate" and generate those rapidly alternating currents used for actual broadcasting. (De Forest had used an electric arc to send his signals.)

When it was found, in 1912, that de Forest's tube could be made to "oscillate," the forgotten dreams of earlier inventors became possible. The Nipkow disk could be made practical. An electric impulse could be amplified a hundred million times and more!

During the First World War, the de Forest tube was improved as rapidly as possible, under the stress of military necessity. It was used on land and sea, in telephone, telegraph, and radio. It was used above the earth in airplanes, and beneath the sea in submarines. Both surface vessels and submarines employed it in radio devices called "hydrophones." This apparatus used two microphones, sticking out from the ship's bottom, to pick up the sound of a submarine's propellers (or vice versa) and determine its location.

By 1920, de Forest's radio tube had been so much improved that it became a major factor in the rapid growth of radio broadcasting during the 1920's.

De Forest was making history, but he was not alone.

Hans Knudson had sent a drawing by radio for the first time in 1909. In the same year, the S.S. *Republic* collided with the S.S. *Florida* outside New York harbor, and summoned aid by wireless.

In 1910, Enrico Caruso and Emmy Destinn sang over the de Forest radiophone from backstage at the Metropolitan Opera House. They were heard as far away as Connecticut, and by a ship at sea. An airplane flying over New York City sent the first wireless message from above the earth in 1910.

Two years later the S.S. *Titanic* struck an iceberg, on its maiden voyage. Although hundreds perished for want of lifeboats, wireless made it possible to call for help— and 705 survivors were rescued. The *Titanic's* message was heard in New York by a young wireless operator named David Sarnoff, who was later to become President of RCA, the Radio Corporation of America.

In November, 1916, New Rochelle, a suburb of New York, got its first radio station—2ZK, operated by George C. Cannon and Charles V. Logwood. Music from 9 to 10 P.M., daily except Sundays.

On July 31, 1918, the United States government—at war—took over the control and operation of nearly every radio transmitter in the country—for the duration. When the Armistice was signed, it was announced by wireless from Germany and France.

Vacuum tube transmitters began to come into general use in 1919—year of the formation of the Radio Corporation of America.

In August, 1920, the following article appeared in the magazine, *The Wireless Age.*

From England comes announcement of . . . developments in wireless transmission . . . bordering upon the realm of the fantastic and marvelous. H. Grinnell Matthews, an English experimenter, avers that he has made encouraging progress with a television device which will make it possible to witness, almost instantaneously, events that are actually happening far away. . . . However the television announcement was skeptically received by some American wireless experts. Dr. Alfred N. Goldsmith, secretary of the Institute of Radio Engineers, doubts whether this wonder is to come to pass. . . .

Needless to say, he was wrong. To be sure, Mr. Matthews' device does not seem to have gotten into print again, but television and Dr. Goldsmith have. Today, Goldsmith is a leading American authority on television and radio.

1920 was the year in which radio broadcasting, as an industry, really began. On August 20, Station WWJ opened up in Detroit. On November 2, Station KDKA, in Pittsburgh, inaugurated its regular schedule, featuring the broadcast of election returns in the 1920 presidential campaign—when the Republican ticket, Warren G. Harding and Calvin Coolidge, won by a "landslide" over the Democratic ticket, James Cox and Franklin D. Roosevelt. But Mr. Roosevelt, who had served brilliantly as Assistant Secretary of the Navy in the Wilson administration, was—like television—destined to get in his licks.

The broadcast of the Harding-Cox election returns caught the fancy of the American public. It started the radio broadcasting industry on its meteoric and golden path.

Station KDKA, which did the program, had had its beginnings back in 1912 when Dr. Frank Conrad started to tinker with wireless in his garage. During the war he developed a system of trench and aerial telephone, and after the Armistice he put his transmitter-in-the-garage back on the air—playing phonograph records and reading news reports. This metamorphosed into Westinghouse station, KDKA, and the election broadcast came from the transmitter in Conrad's garage.

Inspired by the Harding-Cox election broadcast, and activated by de Forest's tube, radio became a fad. Thousands of people clamped on earphones and scratched away at "crystals," with a "cat's whisker." They heard squeals and singings, squawks and music, news and static. Amateur enthusiasts built their own sets—called themselves "hams." People without sets gathered in other people's homes to hear this wireless gadget.

The fad turned into an industry. Set manufacturers, tube manufacturers, earphone manufacturers, they all began to show fat profits. Everyone except Lee de Forest was cleaning up! While others were making money on his invention, he was in need of it—as he went on to new inventions and experimented with a combination sound on film and talking picture.

In 1922, approximately 400,000 radio sets were in use in the United States. That figure skyrocketed. Two decades later, a total of 80,000,000 radio sets had been constructed in this country.

The first *commercial* radio broadcast tapped the rainbow, with the pot of gold, in 1922. Station WEAF, of New York City, broadcast an advertisement of the Queensboro Realty Company. It was successful. It started something!

But where was television?

Television was trying to recover from the effects of the First World War and trying to keep alive in the money-grabbing 1920's. It was snowed under by the opportunities for quick profit in radio, movies, automobiles, Florida, oil, Wall Street, and the national administration.

Nevertheless, men were working at television, and the improvement of the radio tubes and multi-stage amplifiers revealed new possibilities. Men were working— Charles Francis Jenkins in Washington, D. C., John Logie Baird in London, Denoys von Mihaly in Budapest. And a most important idea was being worked out by a Russian emigré named Zworykin, who was living in Greenwich Village, New York City. He was going to take the theories of Rosing, Campbell-Swinton, and Einstein and put them to work in television.

CHAPTER NINE

*How Television Almost Replaced Florida, Only
Wall Street Got There First*

IN 1923 when the great American spree was
starting, Charles Francis Jenkins, of Washington, D. C.,
a pioneer in television since 1890, was sending crude
black and white silhouette pictures by radio. Using a
Nipkow disk, he sent a photo of President Harding a
distance of 130 miles—from the Naval Radio Station in
Washington to the Evening Bulletin Building, in Philadelphia.

Captain Richard Ranger was developing his system
of *facsimile* for sending still pictures by radio. In 1924,
he sent photos of President Coolidge, Prime Minister
Stanley Baldwin, and the Prince of Wales, from London
to New York. The whole transmission took twenty
minutes. On May 7, 1925, he took the same length of
time to send maps and photos of war games from New
York to Honolulu, a distance of more than 5000 miles. A
year later, he sent a $1000 check from London to New
York, and it was cashed by the Bankers Trust Company.
Even the citadels of high finance fell before photoradio.

In 1925, both Jenkins in Washington and John Logie Baird in London were sending moving silhouette pictures. These were outlines only, in black and white, with no detail.

What appears to have been the first demonstration of real television—the sending of moving images which showed actual detail—was given by Baird, on January 27, 1926.

The next day the *London Times* wrote:

Members of the Royal Institution and other visitors to a laboratory in an upper room in Frith Street, Soho, on Tuesday saw a demonstration of apparatus invented by Mr. J. L. Baird.

First, on a receiver in the same room as the transmitter, and then on a portable receiver in another room, the visitors were shown recognizable reception of the movements of . . . a person speaking. The image, as transmitted, was faint and often blurred, but substantiated a claim that through the "Televisor," as Mr. Baird has named his apparatus, it is possible to transmit and reproduce instantly the details of movement, and such things as the play of expression on the face.

John L. Baird continued to make history. By the end of 1926, he had developed something which sharply pointed to television's use in future wars. He made television "see" in the dark.

It was described in the February 5, 1927, issue of the English magazine *Nature*, by Alexander Russell:

. . . Mr. Baird has now developed a method by which the image of the person is transmitted, although he is in complete darkness. This result is obtained by flooding the "sending" room by *infra* red rays. . . . One of us stayed in the sending room with a laboratory assistant in apparently complete darkness. In the receiving room, on another floor, the image of the assistant's head was shown brilliantly illuminated on a screen, and all the motions he made could be readily followed.

The images were not outlines or shadowgraphs, but real images. . . . The application of these rays to television enables us to see what is going on in a room which is apparently in complete darkness. So far as I know, this achievement has never been done before.

. . . The direct application of Mr. Baird's invention in warfare to locating objects apparently in the dark seems highly probable, but I hope that useful peace applications will soon be found for it.

The use of this invention in war may have been realized sooner than Mr. Russell feared.

These days were early ones for sound-radio broadcasting, as well as for television. In the United States, the rapid, uncontrolled building of radio stations was causing trouble. Any transmitter could broadcast on any frequency, even if it interfered with other stations. A radio policeman was needed to untangle the traffic jam and keep it untangled. In 1926, the Federal Radio Commission was created, by act of Congress, to be the traffic cop of broadcasting. It was later converted into F.C.C.—the Federal Communications Commission.

The first great radio network started in 1926. The National Broadcasting Company was organized on November 1st, and the Columbia Broadcasting System began operation ten and a half months later.

In 1926, people were using the clichés "radio has arrived," and "radio has come of age," in favor of the more hoary prediction that "radio is a coming thing." That tarnished phrase was transferred to television a few years later, when several dozen million conversationalists and writers-of-letters-asking-for-television-jobs began to nod sagely and opine that it was a smart idea to "get-in-on-the-ground-floor-of-television"!

An innovation in motion pictures was just making its bow to the public, too. Something called "Vitaphone" —the squawkies! On August 7, 1926, the first demonstration was given in New York by Warner Brothers. The event was described by Harold B. Franklin:*

For the opening program Mr. Will Hayes appeared on the screen and, in words perfectly timed to the motion of his lips, greeted the audience and expressed the belief that Vitaphone would revolutionize the motion picture industry. Thus the invention announced its own destiny and compelled the realization that commercial synchronization of motion pictures with voice and music was practical—had graduated from the laboratory. . . . The crux of it all, the feature picture, with its synchronized musical score . . . was *Don Juan,* an instant hit, greeted by an enthusiastic audience. . . . Vitaphone had arrived!

Perhaps Mr. Franklin was a few years ahead of the times when he wrote those words in 1929—as the President of Fox West Coast Theatres. It took the motion picture industry about five years of steady work after that first Vitaphone demonstration before really good talkies began to reel off the production line.

Of the early talkies, the British film critic and producer, Paul Rotha, wrote in 1930:**

. . . a mechanical means of theatrical presentation of spectacles superior commercially to the stage. . . . A degenerate

* *Sound Motion Pictures* by Harold B. Franklin, Doubleday, Doran, 1929.
** *The Film Till Now*, Jonathan Cape, London, 1930.

and misguided attempt to destroy the real use of the film.
. . . The sole aim of their producers is financial gain, and for
this reason they are to be resented.

The television highlight of 1927 came in April, when
engineers of the American Telephone and Telegraph
Company sent pictures and synchronized voice from
New York to Washington and back again—applying
sight to the telephone. People in New York and Washington could see each other as they chatted.

They used a mechanical method of scanning, following in the footsteps of Nipkow. In texture and quality,
the picture had *fifty*-line "definition." This was what is
called "low-definition" television. The sharpness of a
picture, its texture and the fineness of detail, is determined in part by the number of "lines of definition."

Mechanical scanning methods were improved in the
next few years. By 1929, mechanical disks were producing a picture with ninety lines. A few years later, it was
possible to get up to 240 lines by mechanical methods.
This was about as high as engineers were able to get with
the Nipkow disk, or any of its descendants. To increase
the lines of definition, it is necessary to increase the number of revolutions per second of the revolving disk. A
piece of machinery can go just so fast, and no faster—
without breaking down.

The fifty-line quality of television pictures in 1927
did not produce satisfactory pictures. Images were
blurred and flickering. Even 240-line pictures were unsatisfactory. Not until Zworykin's camera came into
use, after 1933, would there be satisfactory pictures. But
in 1927, only a few people knew that. The rest had to
find out the hard way.

Shortly after the beginning of 1928, Baird performed another sensational experiment. On February 8, twenty-seven years after the first Marconi radio signal crossed the Atlantic, John Baird sent the first television picture from England to America.

A woman sat before Baird's camera, with its revolving scanning disk, in his London laboratory. The low definition pictures were broadcast from a shortwave station in Coulsdon. In Hartsdale, a suburb of New York, R. M. Hart turned on his receiver and saw her face. The picture was not good, but it was recognizable.

Three days later the *New York Times* wrote:

Baird was the first to achieve television at all, over any distance. Now he must be credited with having been the first to disembody the human form optically, and electrically flash it piecemeal at incredible speed across the ocean, and then reassemble it for American eyes.

His success deserves to rank with Marconi's sending of the letter "S" across the Atlantic. . . . As a communication, Marconi's "S" was negligible; as a milestone in the onward sweep of radio, of epochal importance. And so it is with Baird's first successful effort in transatlantic television.

The most bizarre of his experiments, however, came on February 10—two days after the transmission to America.

An operation on a boy in London had necessitated the removal of one of the child's eyes. Baird got the surgeon to give him the eye as soon as it was taken out. He hurried to his studio and, according to reports, placed the eye in his apparatus in place of the camera.

Baird is quoted by Orrin Dunlap:

Then I turned on the current and the waves carrying television were broadcast from the aerial. The essential image for television passed through the eye within half an hour after the operation. On the following day the sensitiveness of the eye's visual nerve was gone. The optic was dead. Nothing was gained from the experiment. It was gruesome and a waste of time.*

That John Baird was making a habit of making news is, perhaps, an understatement. A month after the transatlantic experiment, he put a receiving set on the great ocean liner, *Berengaria*. The wireless operator—in midocean—looked in at his sweetheart as she sat in Baird's London studio.

In June, Baird took the first outdoor television pictures, using sunlight for illumination. In July, engineers of the Bell Telephone laboratories in the United States duplicated the feat. And on August 22, engineers of the General Electric Company in Schenectady took their cameras to Albany, capital of the State of New York, to watch Governor Alfred E. Smith accept the Democratic nomination for President. This was the first "remote" television pick-up on record.

At the same time, in London, Baird was demonstrating the first crude systems of television in color and in three dimensional, stereoscopic relief.

On September 11, 1928, the first television drama was broadcast from the General Electric laboratories in Schenectady, New York. In these laboratories Dr. Ernst F. W. Alexanderson had long been at work on television —one of the leading radio scientists in the United States.

The play was an old melodrama *The Queen's Messenger*, by J. Hartley Manners. The cameras of 1928

* *The Outlook for Television*, Harper, 1932.

could "see" only a small area and were not easily moved. Three cameras were used. Two were focused on the heads of each of the two members of the cast. The third was trained on the "props," and the hands which manipulated them. These hands were supplied by two additional actors—their hands "doubling" for those of the two actors, whose heads were seen. The director of the show operated the controls, fading each camera in and out at the proper times.

In October, a young California scientist, Philo T. Farnsworth, was mentioned in the newspapers. Like Zworykin, he was developing a new kind of television receiver, which used a cathode ray tube. Farnsworth went on to develop a type of cathode ray camera different from Zworykin's. It is called the "image dissector." The first type of "dissector" tube had been patented in Germany by Dieckmann and Hell in 1925.

In 1929, other things happened besides a stock market crash in Wall Street.

On February 1st, for instance, the first regularly scheduled international radio broadcast took place, from Queen's Hall, London. Later in the year, short-wave radio from Little America, Antarctica, announced that Admiral Richard E. Byrd and his men had flown over the South Pole.

In June, Dr. Herbert Ives, of Bell Telephone laboratories, demonstrated a color television method.

1929 saw the beginning of television in Germany, by the German Reichspost, using Baird-type equipment.

At the end of September, the British Broadcasting Corporation and Baird's company began to work together, inaugurating an experimental television service.

In November, Zworykin demonstrated his new cathode ray television receiving set. He called it a "kinescope"—from the Greek word "kineo" meaning movement, and the Greek word "scope" meaning observation.

A decade later, when RCA began building television receivers for sale, the "kinescope" was standard equipment for reproducing the pictures. When we come to Chapter Thirteen describing the receiving set, we shall see how it works. It has no moving parts and is easily controlled by the viewer. It is noiseless, has plenty of brilliance, does not flicker, and—most important—gives a good picture.

When Zworykin introduced his kinescope to the Institute of Radio Engineers in 1929, he said, "All the processes needed for projecting motion pictures (by television) are in existence. The theory is all right, but at present the apparatus would have to be endless, cumbersome, and uncertain. But it will be simplified. It will take some years. . . ."

As the year 1930 opened, Ernst Alexanderson, of General Electric, was preparing a new experiment in Schenectady, New York. On February 18, he sent a picture—a rectangular design—all the way to Australia and back again. The round trip took about an eighth of a second—and the design was still recognizable when it finished the trek.

At the end of March, in England, the BBC and John Baird began broadcasting both picture and sound *together* for the first time.

In April in New York City, Herbert Ives at the Bell

Telephone laboratories demonstrated a television-telephone booth. Persons seated in telephone booths three miles apart connected by wire could see each other simultaneously.

Although the "television-telephone" experiment was never put into commercial service, it gave rise to the popular conception that the first appearance of television would be with the telephone company. It would invade the privacy of the home—no longer could one answer the telephone while sitting in the bathtub. That was still as far "around the corner" (new cliché!) as was "prosperity"!

Scientists were beginning to demonstrate television pictures on large screens. Also in April, 1930, Ulysses A. Sanabria showed pictures on a screen two feet square, in Chicago. Baird was working on a picture two feet by five feet in size. On May 22nd, Dr. Alexanderson set up a six by seven foot screen in a Schenectady theater and put on a vaudeville show for the audience. An important part of his apparatus was a light valve which supplied illumination brilliant enough to illuminate a large screen. This valve had been invented the year before by Dr. August Karolus, of Germany. It was an improved form of a much older device known as the "Kerr Cell"—invented back in 1875, by John Kerr, of England.

At the time of this demonstration, Alexanderson said:

Looking back of the development of the electrical industry, we can clearly trace the forces which have enabled the science of electricity to give birth to the electrical industry. We see later how the electrical industry took hold of another branch of science and created the radio industry. . . . For fifteen years radio was simply an auxiliary to navigation. In 1915 and 1916, we held daily communication by radio telephone from Schenectady to New York. We found that many amateurs adopted the habit of listening. . . . But we had no idea to what it would lead. Our idea was to telephone across the ocean, and so we did at the close of the war, but we failed to see the great social significance of broadcasting.

Television is today [1930] in the same state as radio telephone was in 1915 . . . the development of television is inevitable on account of the forces working in the scientific world . . . it is a satisfaction to make one's contribution to this evolution even if, in this case, the results should prove to be only a stepping-stone to something else.*

The Vice-President of the American Telephone and Telegraph Company, Dr. Frank B. Jewett, also issued a statement on television, in 1930. He believed that the right clue to television had not yet been found and perfected.

He said, "Television has not progressed beyond the experimental stage. . . . Television is a reality in America, as it is apparently in London, but it is not commercially practical."

All the television demonstrations in 1930 used mechanical cameras with moving parts—Nipkow disks in one form or another. None of them produced a good enough picture to make television broadcasting practical at that time or with that method. They were stepping-stones to the future.

Another signpost to the future, which made bigger headlines in 1930, was announced on June 22. A $250,-

* This and the following statement are quoted by Orrin Dunlap in *The Outlook for Television*, Harper, 1932.

000,000 Radio City, within the city of New York, was to be built.

On New Year's Day, 1931, there began the first of a ten-year series of broadcasts, combining an empty booming sound and Fascist propaganda. The new year was ushered in by the voice of Il Duce heard in the United States for the first time, as it was broadcast from the short-wave station in Rome. Even then Mussolini was beaten to the draw. The Premier of Japan had spoken words of Yuletide love to America by radio, for the first time, a week earlier—on Christmas Day. Exactly eleven years later, Japan overpowered a small garrison of United States marines on Wake Island.

The Fascist dictator's speech also ushered in a ten-year period of gathering tensions, preparations for war, aggression, destruction, and international hara-kiri culminating in Pearl Harbor. In this decade radio science became a gargantuan thing, serving equally for peace and for war.

But back in 1931, there was a blissfully ignorant white dove of peace perched on the microphones of every land—or so it seemed. This little dove had been cooing a song of quick profit through American microphones.

In fact, microphones—U. S. style—provided one of the very few opportunities of expanding profits in that second year of the great depression.

A lot of people began to visualize a photo-electric son of a peace pigeon singing a song of profit in front of the television camera—vintage, 1931. Of a sudden the word T-E-L-E-V-I-S-I-O-N glistened and sparkled. Fantastically optimistic stories were bruited about, spread through the newspapers, magazines, books. Television companies sprouted, sold stock, organized schools, issued brochures. Dozens of eminently sound and respectable corporations decided to get into television. Perhaps the television picture was not too good yet, but it might develop quickly, on a hundred million shoestrings. Look what had happened to radio between 1921 and 1931!

The word "television" became DYNAMIC!!! It took on the attributes of a Lost Atlantis, a Fountain of Youth, a modern Midas Touch, the THING-TO-GET-IN-ON-THE-GROUND-FLOOR-OF! It would be lighting up every home, competing with the movies. It would KILL the movies! Hollywood executives, used to the vicissitudes of receivership by now—or fearing they soon might be—got the jitters. The sale of aspirin mounted, as they wrote clauses into contracts forbidding the use of anything connected with Hollywood or emanating therefrom, thereby, or thereas, from ever appearing on any form of television.

To the movie moguls a menace, to others it held out the allure of a Brünnehilde a-slumbering in the flaming crucible of science. A lot of people wanted to play Siegfried and rouse the maiden who slept.

Large sums of money were spent for *systematic* research and experiment, to learn more about television, to see what could be done with it.

The leading broadcasting companies, the big electrical companies, pioneer inventors like Jenkins, de Forest, and

Hogan, newspapers, and even Purdue University took up the challenge and took the air.

In 1931, at least fifteen companies had television broadcasting schedules in the United States alone. The Jenkins Television Corporation went on the air, on April 26th—in the middle of a thunderstorm.

In England, John Baird took his portable equipment to Epsom Downs that June and televised England's greatest horse race—the Derby. The following year he televised it again and reproduced it on an eight by ten foot screen in London's Metropole Cinema theater.

The Columbia Broadcasting System put its experimental station, W2XAB, on the air on July 21, 1931—inaugurating an elaborate and costly broadcasting schedule of considerable length.

In Chicago, television stations owned by the Western Television Corporation and by the Chicago Daily News were on the air.

In Los Angeles, the Don Lee radio broadcasting company was already pioneering in television. Its experimental station, W6XAO, began a ten-year period of operation.

In September, U. A. Sanabria was showing television pictures on a ten-foot screen at the Radio Electrical World's Fair in New York.

In the basement of a house in Upper Montclair, New Jersey, youngish Allen Du Mont was experimenting with cathode ray tubes. His previous television work with C. F. Jenkins and Lee de Forest had convinced him of the need to make the cathode ray tube commercially practical.

The RCA station, W2XBS, had moved to the top of the Empire State Building in New York and was broadcasting experimentally.

With the boom in television publicity, writers, executives, directors, actors, engineers, prophets by the score put themselves on record that "TELEVISION IS HERE."

Then, towards the end of 1932, there came a slackening of enthusiasm. Something was wrong. Television was not taking hold.

On February 25, 1933, the Columbia Broadcasting System announced the suspension of its television broadcasts until better equipment was available. The station had been on the air for more than 2,500 hours, over a period of a year and a half. CBS announced that its television work would continue in the laboratory—which it did.

Other television broadcasters were doing the same thing. What had looked like a boom collapsed.

Why?

The main reason was it was not good enough. The mechanical camera, with the revolving Nipkow disk, could not produce a satisfactory image. It flickered and strained the eyes. It was difficult to see anything. As soon as the novelty wore off, viewers lost interest and returned to the more satisfactory pictures available in any movie theater. The broadcasters had the wrong system. They would have to develop something else.

By 1933, the pinch of the depression had exerted its pressure, too. More laboratory work, more experimentation to find a better television camera meant the expenditure of a lot more money. The illusion of easy profits in television began to look as promising as Wall Street, or the outlook for world peace.

But there was money to be made in good old radio, and in sound movies—immediate money, quick money, big money. So, television was hushed up, smiled away, hustled out like a little dog which had disgraced itself in the parlor.

The promoters passed it back to the inventors, and waited to see what would happen.

As far as the public was concerned, it left only a sense of vague confusion in the air. Television, did you say? Wonderful . . . wonderful. . . . No end to the wonders of science. . . . Have to buy a set when it arrives, but that won't be for years and years. . . . Say, who is that little guy over in Germany I've been reading about, the guy with the Charlie Chaplin mustache. . . ?

This was the beginning of 1933.

Television was stymied. Stymied until the Radio Corporation of America brought out a new camera, perfected by Vladimir Zworykin. It was called the "iconoscope"—a name derived from the Greek word "icon," meaning image, and "scope," meaning observation.

Zworykin had started work on it in 1923, and the main patent was applied for in 1925 and granted in 1928. After a decade of research, experiment, and improvement —and after a reputed cost to RCA of more than $4,500,000—it was to break an impasse for the frustrated television industry.

Its inventor, Vladimir Kosma Zworykin, a young Russian emigré living in Greenwich Village, had graduated from the Technological Institute of St. Petersburg in 1912, where he had studied under Boris Rosing. During the First World War, he served in the Signal Corps of the Russian Army. In 1919, he arrived in the United States and started work at the Westinghouse laboratories the following year.

In 1923, he figured out an idea for a cathode ray tube camera, following the general theory described by A. A. Campbell-Swinton in 1907 and 1908. Apparently he had trouble getting money to develop it, until he met David Sarnoff, head of RCA. Sarnoff saw its possibilities, and Zworykin joined RCA to perfect his cathode ray camera.

Zworykin narrowly avoided an abrupt end. He had planned to install an early model of his iconoscope in the dirigible *Akron*. The plan was to fly above the clouds, then lower the camera, on a cable, until it was below the cloud level. The officers of the *Akron* could see what was going on below without exposing the dirigible to view. For one reason or another, the test was postponed. In the meantime, the *Akron* went on its fatal flight— and crashed.

The iconoscope was completely different from the television cameras then in use. It had no moving parts of any sort. Zworykin had re-examined the human eye and made a device to *duplicate* its functions. It broke the log jam, and opened a new road for television. It was the first satisfactory electric eye for seeing-at-a-distance.

To be sure, there was a second basic type of cathode ray camera being developed at the same time, in another laboratory, Philo T. Farnsworth's "dissector" tube.

The iconoscope and the dissector had become the most important television cameras in the world by 1935. Television systems, in nearly every country, were to be based on the fundamental patents of Zworykin or Farnsworth or both.

Improvements and variations on the two methods have been coming out ever since, but the basic principles remain the same.

Of the two, Zworykin's iconoscope was the first. Undoubtedly, it was the most widely used method and most important for television audiences of the late 1930's and the 1940's.

On the receiving end, cathode ray receivers, such as Zworykin's kinescope, were the most important for the same audiences.

Therefore, let us concentrate on the iconoscope and the kinescope. This is not intended to disparage any of the other systems, which we can only mention in passing. To do otherwise would mean an involved technical discussion.

While television was getting a set of workable eyes, it was getting good ears, too. A number of varieties appeared on the market—"dynamics," "crystals," "velocities," "carbons," and "condensers." Again, in the interests of simplicity, let us concentrate on just one type— the kind most familiar to radio audiences of the 1940's— the "velocity" or "ribbon" microphone.

Since these new inventions revolutionized television throughout the world after 1933, it is important that we take a look at them. Doubly so, since their effect on your life will be far reaching and revolutionary.

First, a glance to see what makes television tick. Then

to see what happened to it in a world plunging inexorably into war, to watch the changes it set in motion as an instrument of war and a priceless heritage for peace, in the United States, in England, Russia, Germany, Japan, Italy, France, Canada, Holland, Sweden.

CHAPTER TEN

Listen to Voices in the Upper Air
(Nor Lose Thy Simple Faith in Mysteries)

BY now, we have assembled a sizable pile of information, sorted out in chronological order. It represents the disassembled parts of television. The basic inventions have all been made, so let's put the pieces together and see what happens. After we know what television is, we shall see what happened to it in a world at war.

In setting down this general impression of the way television works, the objective is simplicity with accuracy. Certain complicated processes, such as thermionic emission and Einstein's quantum theory, have been reduced to graphic, everyday illustrations which show the net effect produced by these processes. Should the technician be nettled by such simplification, let him remember that we are interested in getting a clear, concise idea of television—and not in getting involved in the complicated mathematics of electronic concepts.

At the very beginning of this book, television's goal was established. The human ear and eye had to be duplicated—electrically. It has taken thousands of years to get to the goal, but finally it has been reached:

First—consider those foolish looking things on either side of your head.

When the ear was investigated, in the Prologue, we started by making a sound—the result of striking a table. Sound waves traveled through the air in all directions, like ripples in a pool of water after a pebble is tossed into it. When these sound waves reach your eardrum, they made it vibrate. The eardrum passed the vibrations along until they reached sensitive nerves. These nerves converted the vibrations into nerve currents and sent them along to your brain, where they were "heard."

Television hears in very much the same way, but it has a metal ear—the microphone.

The "eardrum" of the microphone is a thin *ribbon* of a metal alloy called duralumin. It is even thinner than tissue paper, being only $\frac{1}{10,000}$ of an inch thick. It is so delicate that when sound vibrations pass it in the air, the ribbon vibrates with them, like an eardrum. Back and forth it moves, vibrating in perfect harmony with the sound waves.

Here is where the microphone begins to differ from the ear and substitutes its own duplicate system. The important thing in this duplicate system is that *the metal ribbon is suspended in the air between two magnets*. Thereby hangs the tale.

You remember magnets radiate what are called "invisible lines of magnetic force." Even though we cannot see these lines of force, which fill the air around a magnet, we know they exist. For instance, we can see and feel them pulling at other pieces of metal. In the same way we know wind exists, even though we cannot see it. We feel it and see it blowing our hats away.

If two magnets are placed close together, there are going to be a great many lines of force in the space between them. This is true of the magnets in a microphone.

At the date peg of 1831, Michael Faraday discovered

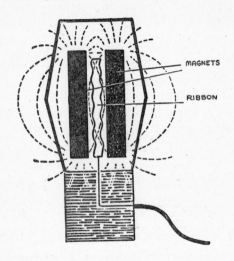

what happened when a "conductor," such as a piece of steel, moved through a magnetic field. It broke lines of force, and that caused an electric current to be generated in the piece of metal!

The ribbon in the microphone is metal, and it hangs right in the middle of many lines of magnetic force. When it vibrates back and forth, in harmony with the sound waves in the air, only one thing can happen. Obviously, since it moves forward and back, *it is breaking through lines of force. Therefore, an electric current is generated in the ribbon.*

More than that, the ribbon moves in such perfect harmony with the sound waves that this current varies according to the slightest changes in the sound. As a result, *the current is an exact record of the sound waves*, but it is now "piped" through a wire as a series of electrical impulses, running one after another in a steady procession.

This current is, of course, very weak when it leaves the microphone. It must be strengthened, *amplified*, in order to stand the rigors of a long journey. So it pays a visit to the amplifiers.

In fact, it goes through a number of amplifiers and is strengthened many millions of times before it is ready to be radiated out through the air from the transmitter.

These amplifiers, so vital to radio and television, grew from the radio tube invented in 1906 by Lee de Forest.

After leaving the amplifiers, with considerable gusto, the electric impulses travel through another wire to the transmitting station. It is here that the electrical record of the sound, and the electrical record of the pictures, will be pumped out through the air to your home. And you will be surprised to find how it is done.

But first let us see how we get the pictures. That is even more fascinating. How does television see?

CHAPTER ELEVEN

One Picture Is Worth Ten Thousand Words

A THOUSAND miles out on the tossing wastes of the North Atlantic, a finger of steel rises from the waves. Silently it glides along, a trail of bubbles feathering behind. Its one unblinking eye is fixed on the gray hull of a liner.

Beneath the periscope a lever is pulled. A ton of death surges from the snout of the submarine and streaks away, cleaving the surface for half a mile with a scar of foaming white.

The cold, round eye stares after it, until a geyser erupts beside the ship, and the impact of exploding TNT shudders through the water. The finger of steel dips into a wave and is gone.

In a cabin of the liner's top deck, the radio operator's hand is already clicking the key of the emergency wireless—three short clicks. Again he repeats it—three short clicks—and again and again.

The message spurts from the wireless serial, dot-dot-dot, S-S-S, SUBMARINE!

The radio operator spells out the ship's name, and

location. Words are clicked off, letter by letter, in a simple code of dots and dashes. Each time the key is pressed down, an electric circuit is completed, and a burst of current shoots into the wireless transmitter.

This is the Morse code which most of us have seen or heard—in railroad stations, on ships, or on short-wave radio sets. An operator may click his key ten or twelve times a second, spelling out three or four letters in long and short spurts of current.

Broadcasting voices and music is more complicated.

Music is composed of one sound after another, and in one minute there may be thousands of musical sounds. But they come one after another, not all at once, and each sound can be represented by a controlled electrical impulse. It may be a very complex chord, but it is still one musical sound, represented by a single current, with each succeeding sound represented by succeeding single impulses.

In television it takes at least a couple of hundred thousand different electric impulses to represent and record one complete picture.

And to create the illusion of motion in the pictures, there must be from fifteen to thirty complete pictures every second.*

If you wish, you can figure that out yourself. It means, roughly, that in one second of television we must

* Actually, to reduce flicker, it is necessary to divide each *complete* picture into two halves, or *fields*, and reproduce first one field and then the other, by a process known as "interlaced scanning." First the odd numbered lines of definition (1, 3, 5, 7, etc.) are reproduced, and then the even numbered lines are reproduced in the spaces left between the odd lines. The two *fields* are thus "interlaced." In the iconoscope, there are thirty *complete* pictures, "frames," per second, reproduced in two parts—therefore sixty *fields* per second.

create and transmit and turn back into pictures and sound in your home receiving set, 30 times 200,000 electric impulses—or 6,000,000 a second. When you remember that the dot-dash telegraph system only sends around ten impulses in a second, you may suspect that television is somewhat more difficult.

Any method of communication that must send out six million pieces of sound and picture in a second has to work fast. The only thing which can work that fast is electricity. The human eye is electric.

In the eye, the picture is focused on the sight nerves of the retina.* Electric impulses are created in the nerves by the effect of light on them. The currents run through the nerves to the brain. The picture, divided into as many individual parts as there are sight nerves, is apparently transmitted to the brain all at one time.

This was what man had to duplicate, if television was to be achieved.

But if it takes some 200,000 separate impulses to represent one complete picture, does that mean a television camera must have 200,000 wires running to 200,000 separate transmitters? Must there be 200,000 receiving sets-in-one to view a program?

Of course not. That is completely impractical.

The first television systems did try to imitate this, though. That was the method proposed by Carey in 1875.

Not until scientists stopped trying to *imitate* the eye

---

* In order to avoid sounding too complicated in the beginning of the book, the exact number was not mentioned. There are about 130,000,000 nerves, called "rods," which are sensitive only to shape—that is, black and white. And there are about 7,000,000 more, called "cones," which see the colors.

and tried to *duplicate* its powers by a substitute method did they find the first key to television. This happened in 1884 when Paul Nipkow patented his whirling, scanning disk.

The Nipkow disk was limited. In order to get a reasonably good quality picture, it is necessary to transmit about 6,000,000 impulses a second. A revolving metal disk cannot whirl fast enough for that, for machinery cannot stand the strain of such a speed. That was a weak link in the early television systems, and it had to be replaced. For this, we had to wait until the science of electronics was developed more fully. We know how long it was before the world took "electronic television" seriously—not until after Zworykin perfected his iconoscope well along in the 1930's. This long delay existed despite the fact that the principles of television by purely electronic methods, which did away with the scanning disk, were known as early as 1908.

In a nutshell, this is how the camera sees:

The light rays of the picture pass through the lens, which focuses the image on the retina of the iconoscope. As far as this it is just like the eye.

The retina of the iconoscope is called the *mosaic*, for the simple reason that it is made in the form of a mosaic —its surface being a number of little pieces fitted together, like the tiles on the bathroom floor.

The mosaic is made of a sheet of mica, the surface of which is studded with hundreds of thousands of tiny metal globules, or specks—*each one separate and insulated from its neighbor*. They correspond to the ends of the sight nerves, which stud the retina of the human eye.

As in the eye, these metal specks are sensitive to light. They generate an electric charge within themselves whenever light shines on them. Each one is a tiny photo-electric cell, a minute electric eye. The metal of which they are made is a "cousin" of selenium,* which caused so much trouble for that cable operator in Ireland in 1873.

When the picture is focused on the mosaic, an electric charge is developed in every one of the metal specks. The white parts of the picture, having the strongest light, create the biggest electric charges in those upon which they fall. Darker portions of the picture, having less powerful light rays, generate weaker charges in the specks upon which they are focused.

The optical picture has created a complete electrical duplicate of itself in the metal specks, which form the mosaic. Since only a tiny portion of the entire picture will fall on any single speck, this electrical duplicate consists of hundreds of thousands of tiny charges of electricity.**

It will help you to visualize this if you will look at any average half-tone picture in the daily newspaper. At normal reading distance, it looks quite solid, but if you examine it closely you will find it is actually composed of thousands of little dots of ink. If charges of elec-

---

* A cousin, figuratively speaking. Chemically they are quite different. Both are sensitive to light, but react in different fashions.

** Although there are many hundreds of thousands of specks, the charges will eventually be grouped together in about 200,000 little dots—many specks going together to form one dot. This re-grouping is done when the mosaic is scanned by the electron stream.

Therefore, in the interests of simplicity, let us say that the optical picture has created a complete electrical duplicate of itself in the equivalent of some 200,000 separate electrical charges.

tricity were colored like ink, the electrical duplicate on the mosaic might look like a half-tone picture, except that the individual specks are much smaller.

The electrical record of the picture is stored in the mosaic—just as in the eye. However, in the eye each nerve-current (as far as we know) passes through its own individual nerve, which connects directly with the brain. At this point television stops *imitating* the eye

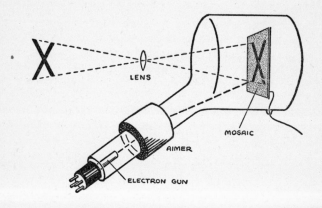

and shifts to its own substitute system, which will enable it to span great distances.

The metal specks of the mosaic, being insulated from each other, each retain their own little charge of electricity. All we have to do now is to collect them, one after another, with a practical system—and do it so rapidly it will seem instantaneous. To do this we use the process of "scanning," of which we have talked before.

As you look at this page, you do not read it all at once, in a split second. You look first at the beginning of the first line, and your eyes *scan* across that line, noting one word after another. At the end of the first line, your eyes jump rapidly back to the beginning of the second line, and then scan across it, with its different words. And so on down the page.

Instead of trying to absorb the entire printed page in one gulp, you separate it into several hundred little parts and read them one after another in the order they appear. As you read this, you are *scanning* the page in the same way the camera *scans* the picture on the mosaic.

In the drawing you will notice something labeled "Electron Gun." This gun is aimed up at the mosaic, from down below, and it shoots out a steady stream of electrons, as a hose shoots out a stream of water.

Next to the electron gun you see something labeled "aimer." This is the "hand" which aims the electron stream, as your hand would aim a garden hose.*

The electron gun is used to *scan* the mosaic in a manner similar to the action your eyes perform as you *scan* this printed page. Of course, it is infinitely more rapid in its scanning speed—about 30,000 times faster than the average reader.

The gun "reads" by spraying the electron-stream across the top line of the mosaic. Then it jumps back and aims the stream across the second line, and the third, and the fourth, and so on. (Actually the process is not quite as simple as this, but for our purposes there is no need to bring in complicated details.)

As the electron stream is aimed across each line in the mosaic, it passes over each photo-electric metal speck,

---

* This "aimer," or deflection coils, aims by the use of electric or magnetic fields, to which electrons are susceptible.

one after another—just as your eye goes across each word in each line of this page.

The electron-stream, like water spurting from a fire hose, packs a wallop. In effect, when it hits each speck, it "knocks" the electric charge, which has been stored there, right out of the speck. It "drives it through" the sheet of mica into the metal plate on the other side. Then the stream moves on to the next speck, and "knocks" its electric charge across to the metal plate. The stream moves on, knocking off the third, the fourth, fifth, right on down the line to the end. Then it whips back to the beginning of the second line, and does the same thing there. After that it continues down the mosaic, "reading" line after line.

The metal plate is connected to a wire. As fast as each little electric charge is knocked through the mica to the plate, it scrambles to its feet and darts away through the wire—to be followed by the second charge, and the next, and the next, until all the 200,000 separate charges are gone.

The picture, which has been converted into an electrical duplicate of itself, in the form of some two hundred thousand minute impulses, has now been "piped" into a wire. These electric impulses, all in regular order, are moving in single file through the wire.

To create the illusion that pictures have motion, we use "persistence of vision." Therefore, we need thirty *complete* pictures a second—for the same reasons that the movies need almost the same number per second, as we learned.

To have thirty *complete* pictures a second in television means that this process of scanning each half of the mosaic must be repeated thirty times in each second. Every speck must be hit by the electron stream and discharged thirty times per second. We have already multiplied 200,000 by 30, and gotten 6,000,000.

The first time you appear before a television camera, you can have the satisfaction of knowing that the light, reflected from your face, carries a picture of you into the camera. There it is focused on the "back wall," the mosaic. Then it is converted into 200,000 separate electrical impulses, which, after being knocked through a mica sheet to a metal plate, run off through a wire, single file.

Since there are thirty pictures a second, and the process must therefore be repeated for each picture, your face will go flashing away through a wire in 6,000,000 different electrical currents in every second.

These currents are strengthened in amplifiers, as the "sound" currents are, and the next step is the transmitting station, where they will be pumped out through space to your home.

CHAPTER TWELVE

At a Distance

WHEN the processions of electric impulses, representing sound and picture, arrive at the sending station, both are broadcast simultaneously on their own private transmitters. Both sight and sound are transmitted in pretty much the same way, except the sight transmitter has to handle a great deal more traffic than the sound transmitter.

Stretching far up into the sky above the transmitter is the aerial, or group of several aerials, for sight and for sound. Television aerials are familiar sights in large cities. Observing New Yorkers have long been familiar with the eight T-shaped rods protruding from the spire of the Chrysler Building, giving it the aspect of a giant hatrack. This is the antenna system of CBS television station, WCBW, the studios of which are in Grand Central Terminal.

The aerials of NBC station WNBT are on the top of the Empire State Building, perched like a Christmas tree ornament on the never-used dirigible mooring mast. From the roof of 515 Madison Avenue has sprouted a red and white steel structure 165 feet high, as though some giant were drilling for oil down the elevator shaft. It is the aerial system of the Du Mont television station, WABD.

Into the aerial of a radio or television transmitter runs a powerful alternating current—a current which flows first in one direction, then reverses and goes in the other direction. It repeats this process very rapidly, back and forth many times a second.

Most electric lights in our homes run on an alternating current. Light current usually alternates at 60 *cycles* —back and forth sixty times per second—too fast for the eye to notice. In some country districts, however, the current alternates at 25 cycles per second, and at this slower speed you can see a decided flicker in the light.

The current in the aerial of a radio or television station alternates much more rapidly, depending on the *frequency* (rapidity of current alternation) for which it is adjusted. For instance, if a station is listed on your dial at 88, or 880 kilocycles—and we know the word *kilo* means thousand—then we know that the antenna current alternates 880,000 times a second in that station.

Television transmitters are tuned to even higher frequencies, and alternate still faster. The word megacycle means a million cycles, or 1,000 kilocycles, and if a television station is tuned to 60 megacycles, its antenna current oscillates 60,000,000 times a second.

Perhaps, when you were reading about the discovery which Hans Christian Oersted made in 1819, you did not realize it would lead all the way to this. Oersted discovered, you remember, that if a current was running through a wire, it caused invisible lines of magnetic force to spread out from that wire in concentric circles. The greater the current, the greater the magnetic field around the wire.

And that led, in 1831, to Faraday's discovery of the principle of *induction,* which is the principle upon which the microphone and the entire system of radio-television transmission is based.

Now, think what this means when you apply it to a television transmitter. The alternating current in the antenna is very powerful. As a result, there are powerful lines of electro-magnetic force spreading out in all directions from the antenna.

This current, though, is alternating back and forth at the rate of, say, 60,000,000 cycles a second. Just imagine what that does to the lines of force.

When the current flows up into the aerial, the lines of force spread out. Then, when the current reverses, these first lines of force collapse and are "sucked" back. A new set shoots out to replace them. This process occurs *every* time the current changes its direction—or 60 million times a second.

These magnetic waves travel through the air for many miles, and they are used to *carry* the program to the receiving set.

The two processions of impulses, forming the electrical record of sight and sound, are super-imposed on the back of two "carrier" waves, which transport them through the air like a magic carpet. When the receiving set is reached, the "program impulses" will climb down from the backs of the "carrier" waves, say thanks for the ride, and turn back into sight and sound to entertain you.

You may be wondering how in the world a television receiver can possibly catch those waves as they fly through the air at 186,000 miles per second.

Have you ever watched a lawn sprayer in the park, in the summer time? It sprays water in all directions, and everything around the sprinkler is touched by the water, out to a certain distance. Beyond that the sprinkler does not reach, unless the water pressure is increased.

Radio and television transmitters are something like lawn sprinklers. They spray out electro-magnetic waves in all directions. Everything within the transmitter's range of fifty, or sixty, or seventy miles in all directions is touched by the magnetic waves, the "lines of force," as they are pumped out and sucked back in again, back and forth, with each alternation of the current.

Now, television sets have an aerial attached to them. Usually it is a copper rod, which is a conductor of electricity.

We learned that, when lines of force are broken through by a metal, an electric current is generated. Remember the metal ribbon in the microphone. Remember how electricity is made in a dynamo.

When the magnetic waves hit the aerial of your set on their way out from the transmitter, they create electric currents in the copper rod. As each wave passes the rod on the way out from the transmitter, it starts a tiny current moving along the wire in one direction. Then, when it is "sucked" back, it passes the wire again and generates another current. But, since it is now moving in the opposite direction, going back to the transmitter, the current it generates this time runs in the opposite direction, too.

Every time the "carrier" wave goes back and forth past the aerial, it generates new electric impulses, moving first in one direction and then in the other. In other words, it generates an alternating current.

Since the magnetic waves came directly from the alternating current in the transmitter, these new currents which are *induced* in the aerial are exactly the same as the currents in the transmitter, except they are very weak after such a strenuous flight through the air. When they are deposited in the aerial, still carrying their cargo of sight and sound, they run down the wire and into the receiving set—still in the same order.

Let us see what we have so far.

First, in the microphone and the camera we created an accurate electrical record of the program in the studio. Sight and sound were turned into electric impulses traveling through two wires. After being increased in strength millions of millions of times, by the amplifiers, they were given a piggy-back ride on the backs of some other, stronger, electric currents, which carried them up into the aerials of the sight transmitter and the sound transmitter.

Here they were changed from an electric current into electro-magnetic waves. In this condition they went flying through the air until they hit their target—the antenna of your receiving set.

Then they turned back into electric currents, slid down the wire into the receiver, and climbed down from the backs of their "carriers."

These impulses are still in *exactly* the same order as when they left the microphone and camera. They still have their own individual characteristics. They still carry an accurate record of what the microphone "heard" and the camera "saw."

Now all that remains to be done is to reassemble them in proper order—unscramble them, if you will—and turn them back into their original form, sound and pictures, exactly as they were in the broadcasting studio.

Perhaps you have guessed how we shall do this.

CHAPTER THIRTEEN

Magic at Your Fingertips

WHEN the two processions of electric impulses, carrying the record of sound and picture, slide down the wire into your television set, they each go their own way—to different parts of the apparatus. Both are weak after the flight through space and need a pick-me-up. So, each goes to an amplifier and is pepped up. Then, on to a sort of "clearing house," where the carrier waves are "strained off." The carriers having performed their task, having carried the program impulses from the transmitter through space, over mountains and rivers and cities to the receiving set, are dispensed with.

Each procession is strengthened again, in new amplifiers. When this is done they are ready for the transformation back into sound and picture.

The pictures are created in a cathode ray tube, which is sketched in the diagram on the next page.

At the narrow end of the tube is an electron gun, which sprays out a stream of electrons—as it does in the camera. At the other end of the tube—the broad end—is the screen on which the pictures appear.

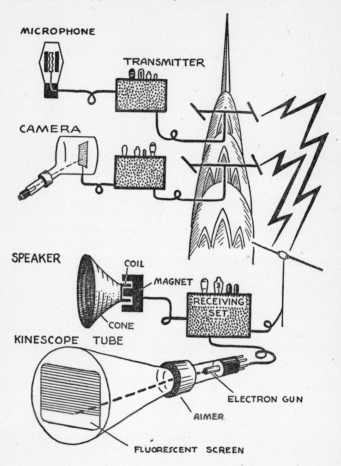

MICROPHONE

TRANSMITTER

CAMERA

SPEAKER

COIL

MAGNET

RECEIVING SET

CONE

KINESCOPE TUBE

ELECTRON GUN

AIMER

FLUORESCENT SCREEN

The procession of impulses, which is the electrical record of all the tiny sections of the picture, is fed into the electron gun. It is the gun's supply of ammunition —just as a machine gun is fed a steady procession of bullets. As each impulse enters the "firing chamber" of the electron gun, it is shot out of the gun and down the tube toward the screen.

This screen is composed of a white, fluorescent substance, which covers the broad end of the tube. The chemical composition of this material is such that it glows for a split second, giving off a pin point of light, whenever it is hit by an electron. So, when the impulses are fired out of the gun, as electron-bullets, they whiz down the tube and hit the screen, creating spots of white light.

Just in front of the electron gun, you will see something labeled the "aimer." It controls the direction of the electron stream, just as in the camera—just as you would aim a garden hose with your hand. The "aimer" can make the electrons land at any point on the screen.

You remember that, in the iconoscope, the electron stream moved back and forth across the mosaic, scanning the image piece by piece. As each piece was scanned, its electrical impulse was sent on its way.

Traveling 186,000 miles a second, the impulses move so fast that the time it takes to reach your receiver is too small to measure. For all practical purposes it is instantaneous.

This being the case, the impulses are shot onto the picture screen at the same time as they are being scanned in the camera.

In addition, the television receiver works in absolute synchronism with the camera. They are in perfect step. When the electron stream scans across the top of the image in the camera, the electron stream in the receiver does likewise. And the electric impulses arrive and are shot on the screen in the same order they were sent out.

As each impulse hits the screen, it makes the fluorescent substance glow, in a spot of white light. If the impulse represents a white part of the original picture, then it creates a pin point of white light of the same brilliance. If the impulse represents a gray spot in the original picture it reproduces a weaker, grayish pin point of light on the screen.

Moving in perfect synchronization with the camera, the electron gun in the tube lays down line after line, until the merging pin points of light build up the entire picture. This is repeated thirty *complete* times a second,* giving the illusion of motion, because of *persistence of vision*—which we discussed before, back in the time of Leonardo da Vinci, 1472.

The picture actually is inside the tube, but since the glass is transparent it is easily seen, as the electron gun "paints" it on the screen.

While the picture is appearing on the screen, the sound is issuing from the loudspeaker.

The procession of impulses, representing the sound, has arrived at the loud speaker, shown in the diagram. In the back of the speaker is an electro-magnet. When a powerful current runs through it, it has a strong magnetic attraction. If the current is weaker, the attraction is weaker.

The procession of impulses varies in strength and character according to the variations in the sound it represents. As the impulses pass through the electro-magnet, they cause its strength to vary as they vary.

---

* As in the camera, interlaced scanning is used. Therefore, thirty complete pictures, or sixty fields per second.

Thus, the magnet's power of attraction is constantly fluctuating.

Set between the poles of the magnet is a coil of wire. It is attached to the large paper cone—which you see immediately when you look at a loudspeaker. This coil of metal wire is subject to the power of magnetic attraction but is separated from the magnet by a narrow gap. As the power of attraction varies, the coil is moved back and forth.

The magnet's attraction fluctuates thousands of times a second. Since the ring is attached to the paper cone, it means that the cone also vibrates. The area of the cone is fairly large, and it causes the air around it to vibrate, too. The vibrations, which correspond exactly to the original sound waves heard by the microphone, turn into sound waves again as the loudspeaker transfers them to the air.

Traveling through the air, they reach your ear—and you hear the sound, as it was in the studio.

Briefly, this is the way television is heard and seen, and sent to your home—so that you may see-at-a-distance.

CHAPTER FOURTEEN

Problems, Problems, Problems

A WORKING solution to the riddle of seeing-at-a-distance had been found. The date peg is 1933—but television was still not ready for the public. Much remained to be done in the way of improvement and refinement, despite the fact that the iconoscope of 1933 was essentially the same as the camera of the 1940's.

Automobiles of 1905 were essentially the same as modern automobiles, save for refinements of the basic designs, but the automobiles of 1905 could immediately be put into commercial use. They could run on *any* kind of road—dirt, gravel, asphalt, concrete, or brick. Television could not be put into commercial use in 1933, for it could not travel over several different kinds of "roads."

Television, as a potential industry and method of communication and entertainment, was faced with problems quite different from those of movies or sound radio broadcasting.

Perhaps an official, government explanation of the situation is in order. James L. Fly explained it in a radio talk, given in his capacity as Chairman of the Federal Communications Commission in 1940. He said:

First let us consider the case of the broadcast of sound alone. Such broadcasting in the United States is roughly twenty years old. As you all know, during these years there has been vast improvement in the technique of radio transmission and reception. There has, however, been no change in the fundamental standards for transmission and reception during that entire period. A receiver built to receive a broadcast station operating in 1920 will receive a broadcast station that operates in 1940. A transmitter built in 1920 will be received by radios in use today. Better transmitters are being built now than were being built in 1920, and the same is true of receivers, but they all operate on the same principle; or, more technically, on the same basic standards. Improvements have been gradual. Obsolescence has taken only a normal toll.

Television is different—uniquely so.

In the case of television, a receiving set is so synchronized with the transmitter that the two are inseparable in operation. The receiving set is, in effect, the key which unlocks the transmitter in order to receive the broadcast. A substantial change in the lock renders the key useless.

A television receiving set capable of receiving the signal of one type of transmitter may not accept the signal of a different type of transmitter in existence today. The receiving set must be constructed to operate on the same principle as the particular transmitter. If the American people should buy television receivers in great numbers as they have bought ordinary radios, and if at a later date transmission standards are adopted which contemplate an alternative or improved transmission system over that on which the particular receivers can operate, we should, in effect, be changing the locks and leaving you with a bunch of highly expensive keys rendered utterly useless.

Television is not the only industry which must be so standardized. All railroad trains in the United States are made to run on the same kind of track—otherwise you would have to change trains dozens of times whenever you took a trip. In the early days of the telephone, there were two different systems. The resulting confusion and duplication of service was such that the telephone business had to be combined into one system. Imagine if you had to have two, or three, or four telephones in your house in order to be able to call your friends, your business, your club.

In 1933, cathode ray tube cameras were comparatively crude. Several different types had been invented, but none were sufficiently advanced to be made the standard for the entire country.

Even though television was not ready for regular commercial broadcasting in 1933, its new eye, the iconoscope, was ready to cause a world-wide revolution in television methods.

The cathode ray tube cameras, in the form of the "iconoscope" and also the "image dissector" of Philo Farnsworth, were the best cameras which had been made. The most successful television systems throughout the world were to be based largely on the patents of either Zworykin or Farnsworth or both.

What happened to television in the United States? What held it back? There have been dozens of rumors, inaccurate stories and speculative articles based on incomplete or superficial information. What are the facts? After we see what really happened in the United States, we can look abroad and find what became of television in England, in France, Russia, Germany, Holland, and a number of other countries—in a world at war.

Let us pick up the story again, from the date peg of 1933. Radio broadcasting had just gone down 2200 feet beneath the surface of the ocean—with William Beebe in his "bathysphere." It was a time when radio was probing into new fields, not only in a physical sense, but in a social sense. On March 12, 1933, President Roosevelt broadcast his first fireside chat—on the banking moratorium, just eight days after he took office.

In April, the U. S. Navy dirigible *Akron*—on which Zworykin had planned to test his iconoscope—crashed off the New Jersey coast.

The RCA laboratories had been conducting experimental television broadcasts, using a low definition mechanical system. In 1933, RCA put Zworykin's iconoscope camera and kinescope receiver into use. The old mechanical system had given a picture of 120-line definition. With the advent of the iconoscope it was raised to 240 lines, and the following year to 343 lines.

But this was all laboratory work—done quietly and without much talk. Here, in the mid-1930's, the high pressure publicity of a few years before was shunned. Television was a cloistered mystery of the laboratory, far from the feverish touch of public life and pretty much unsung.

Orrin Dunlap wrote in the *New York Times,* on Sunday, January 5, 1935:

What are the outlooks for television prospects in 1935? That is a question often heard at this season. No prophets are found. Too many staked their reputations and had them badly marred on several occasions. Now, whenever they discuss the elusive television they no longer say with a confident definiteness, "I predict," but with a puzzled look they say, "I believe." The research experts are confident they have television ready to launch. The industrial leaders assert it may be ready scientifically but not economically. Whether they will solve the riddle in 1935 is problematical. The one big problem remains to haunt them; what would happen to the present broadcasting setup, and the millions invested in transmitters, networks, and in 18,000,000 receiving sets? Until someone finds the answer to that puzzle television as a public entertainment in the home is likely to stay timidly in the laboratory and be content to let the hands of science nurture the images to the size and clarity of the motion picture.

Within a few weeks from the time this article appeared, however, the public pulse of television began to beat again.

In February, 1935, American papers carried reports that England was going to establish a public television service without delay. In April, it was reported in the *New York Sun* that the Farnsworth Television Company, of Philadelphia, had signed agreements to interchange patents with the Fernseh company, of Germany. On May 7th, David Sarnoff, President of the Radio Corporation of America, announced his company would spend a million dollars on a series of experimental television test broadcasts from RCA's new transmitter on top of the Empire State Building in New York City. The tests began on June 29th, 1936, and continued throughout that year.

On November 6, 1935, Major Edwin Armstrong, one of America's foremost radio engineers, announced his now famous "FM." He had taken a principle of radio transmission, long known but undeveloped, and perfected a new system of transmitting radio waves. It eliminated static and opened the way for true high fidelity broadcasting. (When the 1941 television standards were established, it was stipulated that the sound should be broadcast by FM.)

In 1936, cathode ray television began to spread beyond the laboratory of its inventors.

The Columbia Broadcasting System in New York ordered an all-cathode ray television system from RCA.

On the other side of the country, in Los Angeles, the Don Lee Broadcasting System began public television demonstrations with cathode ray tube equipment.

In August, the Philco Radio and Television Corporation was demonstrating its cathode ray system in Philadelphia. Through the summer and fall months, the American Telephone and Telegraph Company was laying a new kind of telephone wire between Philadelphia and New York. It was a "coaxial cable," capable of carrying the burden of a television program—too much for ordinary wires. On December 1st, the cable was tested and proved successful; here was one way to establish television networks in the future, to link the individual stations by coaxial cable.

Throughout 1937 the technical development continued without making any headlines. Occasionally stories appeared telling of laboratory miracles—or of the new television broadcasting in London and in Germany.

On May 12, 1937, RCA demonstrated television pictures, 8 by 10 feet in size, projected on a screen. The engineers who gave the demonstration were R. R. Law and Vladimir Zworykin. Previously it had been held that large pictures could be achieved only by mechanical systems—which usually meant poor quality. Now it also could be accomplished with cathode ray tube receivers—with a development of Zworykin's kinescope.

But the interest of the public was on sound radio with its first-hand coverage of the national and international situation: President Roosevelt's "fireside chats," and the 1936 election; the abdication of Edward VIII on December 11, 1936; the crash of the German dirigible *Hindenburg* at Lakehurst, New Jersey, May 6, 1937; the coronation of George VI; the remarkable radio coverage of the 1938 Sudetenland dispute, beginning with Hitler's Nuremberg oration and culminating in Munich.

All this time the progress of American television had been under the general supervision of the Federal Communications Commission. In the Communications Act of 1934, passed by Congress, it was stipulated that:

The Commission, from time to time as the public interests require, *shall*

Study new uses for radio, provide for experimental uses of frequencies, and generally encourage the larger and more effective use of radio in the public interest . . .

Regulate the kind of apparatus to be used with respect to its external effects and the purity and sharpness of the emissions from each station and from the apparatus therein . . .

Make such regulations not inconsistent with law as it may deem necessary to carry out the provision of this Act.

On September 10, 1938, the Commission was asked to consider a proposed set of television engineering standards prepared by the Radio Manufacturers' Association—the trade group of radio manufacturers. A few months later, the Commission appointed its Television Committee, consisting of three Commissioners, to investigate further the status of television and to recommend a course of action.

In the meantime, the Radio Corporation of America, already the strongest power in television, moved to strengthen its position. In October, 1938, it was reported in the papers to have bought the patent rights for television inventions of Harry Lubcke, head of television for the Don Lee Broadcasting System of California. A decade before RCA had co-ordinated its television work with General Electric and Westinghouse. A year later, in 1939, RCA interchanged patents with the Farnsworth Company, and three years later with the Allen B. Du Mont Laboratories.

On the 20th of October 1938, David Sarnoff announced at a board meeting of the Radio Manufacturers Association that RCA was going ahead with television. He pointed out that many problems still confronted those who wanted to establish television, and these problems must be solved before any national service of network programs could be made available. RCA believed they could be solved only by operating experience, so it proposed to go ahead and begin to broadcast a limited series of television programs from its New York television transmitter on the Empire State Building. This transmitter, when placed in operation, radiated its programs out over an area extending roughly from 50 to 60 miles from New York.

RCA also announced its intention of beginning its public television service with a program showing the opening of the New York World's Fair.

Television's future looked bright at the beginning of 1939, if one forgot the implications of Munich and if one failed to take a searching look at the economic problems of television. The scientists had worked for decades to bring television out of the laboratory, but now the broadcasters, the program builders, and the businessmen were faced with an unexpectedly arduous task—to put it across.

The opening of the New York World's Fair, on April 30, 1939 was publicized around the world. That RCA would inaugurate its experimental television program schedule with a broadcast of that event was also well bruited about—even achieving a two-installment article in *Fortune* (April-May, 1939). Quoth *Fortune:*

Television is a big baby, nursed by a corps of able scientists and tickled lovingly under the chin by Wall Street and Hollywood . . . a major technological accomplishment . . . a giant industry a-borning. . . . On April 30, the trumpets will blow and the bands will play and the long parades will start out to the reconditioned Long Island swamp where Grover Whalen is opening his New York World's Fair. But this is not important. For, a long time after the World's Fair has become one of grandfather's stories, April 30 will still be the day when they formally started television service in the U. S. . . . and few dates in history have been better ballyhooed in advance.

You probably will not have a chance to participate in the first day of television service, or even the first month. In spite of the heavy creeping barrage of publicity . . . television won't do more than get in under the wire. Barring acts of God, the National Broadcasting Company's transmitter will be on the air and the public will have a few sets. That is all that has been promised and it is enough—a sort of token payment on things to come.

Despite the formal April opening, television was still in a delicate condition. For one thing, the outbreak of war was only a few months off. For another thing, television broadcasting was strictly experimental. Possibly with this view, the F. C. C. Television Committee issued, on May 22, a report urging caution and co-operation in dealing with television.

The outbreak of war in September, 1939, cast long shadows. To those who saw clearly and with perspective, it was obvious that the United States was involved. Where did that put television? In England, it had just been closed down for the duration, and journalists started to dig up some old obituaries for United States television.

To be sure, there were military reasons, peculiar to England, which had made it necessary to halt the distinguished progress of the British Broadcasting Corporation in vision programs. These problems did not apply in America. In the same way, certain aspects of English radio had made it possible for the BBC to start television broadcasting two and a half years ahead of America. The incongruous result was that the United States was starting just as England was being forced to stop.

The war was not the only element of uncertainty for American broadcasters. The purely domestic, economic problems were perhaps more complex to solve.

On November 15, 1939, the F. C. C. Television Committee submitted a second report. It felt the television industry had not advanced beyond the experimental stage, but it had arrived at a point where more rapid progress might be made if broadcasters were permitted to have programs paid for, in part, by advertisers. The Committee also pointed out that technical development was progressing all the time and nothing should be done to retard it. At the same time, the Committee recommended that:

No interests should be permitted to raise public hopes falsely, nor to encourage public investments where the state of scientific or economic development leaves any doubt that such hopes and expenditures are justified for the use of the public property in the radio spectrum.

This second report was tentatively adopted by the entire Commission on December 22, 1939, and "all interested parties desiring to be heard with respect to these proposed rules" were invited to participate in a public hearing on January 15, 1940.

The hearing revealed a considerable division of engineering opinion over the technical standards proposed by the F. C. C. Different companies disagreed as to just what was the best method of performing certain electronic operations. There was no unanimous agreement as to whose patents were best for each part of the television system. This could only be solved by further experimentation. The representatives of the television industry had to reach an agreement between themselves. When this was accomplished, final standards could be set.

The hearing also underscored the difficult economic problems facing the broadcasters.

In the first place, television broadcasting was expensive and every cent spent was a loss. There was no revenue coming in from television, nor was there likely to be for a number of years. During the hearing it was brought out that RCA had spent more than $10,000,000 on television in the period of 1934 through 1939. CBS reported that, at the end of 1939, it was spending at a rate of about $1,000,000 a year on television—and it had not yet gone on the air.

But this financial drain was not the only problem. There was a much more complex one. The Television Committee of the F. C. C. had asked that television stations offer a "broadcast service to the public." It had also stated that the public should be protected against "quick obsolescence of television receivers."

In order to see these programs, the public would have to buy television receivers. If programs of "high public appeal" were available, that, in itself, would constitute a real incentive to the purchase of sets.

But, the Committee also stressed that "caution should be taken not to give impetus to a rapid purchase by the public of large quantities of receivers, because . . . it may be discovered that considerable changes in the recent technical design may have to be made as a result of practical experience.

The problem this posed was a difficult one. How to develop the industry without subjecting the public to the risk that all its television sets might suddenly become obsolete.

One way out would have been to do nothing, to broadcast no programs at all until the technical transmission standards could be set permanently. That would have protected the public against financial loss, and it would have saved the broadcasters a great deal of money. Unfortunately, it would also have delayed the development of television for an indefinite number of years. There had already been such a delay since 1933.

Paul Kesten, representing the Columbia Broadcasting System, suggested what seemed to be the three most likely courses of action open to American television.

One possible course was to fix the standards, as proposed in the Television Committee's report—to fix them immediately for a stated number of years and allow television broadcasters to proceed with scheduled programs. After the standards were set, it would still be possible to improve the quality of the picture by about 100 per cent by various refinements of design. If the standards were fixed for a stated period, it should be long enough to remove any hindering influence caused by a fear that receiving sets might become useless in three or four years' time.

The second proposed course of action was to delay both the broadcasting of programs and the setting of standards until it could be determined if *flexible* standards were not practical. Such flexible standards would mean that a receiving set could be easily adjusted to receive programs even if the standards were changed.

The third possible course was to go ahead and broadcast programs immediately, without setting any standards. But, if this were done, CBS felt that the public should be warned "actively and frequently" of the risk involved.

This economic and scientific problem of the fixing of standards had to be settled before the American television industry could move ahead on a sound basis—and spend the hundreds of millions of dollars it would take to establish a nation-wide television service.

There were other problems, too. For instance, there was the job of deciding just how a nation-wide, or even a regional, television network would be linked. Would it be linked, as the radio industry is, by special telephone cables? That would warm the cockles of the American Telephone and Telegraph Company's heart. Or, would it be linked by RCA ultra-high frequency radio relay stations—which, needless to say, would please RCA. On the other hand, Hollywood would give a sigh of relief if a "celluloid network" were established— if programs were filmed and rushed throughout the country in cans. Maybe all three methods would be used, or possibly some new, unexpected invention would upset everything.

If in 1940 you had demanded to know where television was, you might have received a rather plaintive echo from television itself, wanting to know the answer, too.

And then, of course, there *was* the war—getting worse all the time. Television might find the answer to its domestic woes and still go down as a war casualty.

The immediate future did look a bit grim, to say the least. Nevertheless the feeling persisted that, in the United States, with its drive toward improvement and social advance, television could not be left neglected and undeveloped.

CHAPTER FIFTEEN

Traffic Lights Are Green and Red

"THE present state of flux of television does not warrant confining standards, but development of the industry does merit limited commercial operations in the near future." This was the unanimous ruling of the Federal Communications Commission following the January, 1940, hearing, and September 1, 1940, was set as the date for the beginning of "limited commercial" operation. The Commission ruled further:

That research should not halt and that scientific methods should not be frozen in the present state of the art is fairly to be deduced from the engineering testimony of representatives of the companies represented at the hearing. . . . Actual demonstrations to members of the Commission indicate the need for further improvement in the technical quality of television. The evidence before the Commission reveals a substantial possibility that the art may be on the threshold of significant advance. Research in fact does and should continue in significant phases of the field.

We feel that potentially television is of tremendous value to the public generally. Even now, there is no reason apparent why those members of the public to whom regular television programs are available, who are conscious of the fluid state of the art, and who are willing to assume the financial risks involved for the obvious benefits of current programs, should not acquire receivers. Nor is it suggested that television broadcasters should be barred from going forward in program production and sponsorship. The progress made by the industry is worthy of recognition, and the present state of the art renders appropriate the further steps permitted by the rules being established.

Beginning September 1st, television stations could begin limited commercial operations, under which advertising would have been permitted in connection with programs the cost of which was borne by sponsors. The rules stressed, however, that emphasis on the commercial aspects of the operation at the expense of program research was to be avoided. The Commission wrote:

Even more important, nothing should be done which will encourage a large public investment in receivers which, by reason of technical advances when ultimately introduced, may become obsolete in a relatively short time. The Commission has not overlooked the significant sums invested by pioneers in making possible our present knowledge of television, and it is not unsympathetic with their desire to recoup their investment in the process of bringing television's benefits to the public. It will be realized, however, that the loss to the public by premature purchase in a rapidly advancing field might in a relatively short period exceed many times the present total cost of research. Such an economic loss in the long run can rebound only to the harm of the industry. In view of the apparent proximity of improvements and of the resolution of disputed technical questions, these risks should not be taken. The Commission is, therefore, reserving the matter of issuing standards for consideration at some future time.

The newspapers hailed it as "the green light" for television.

The television industry continued to go forward with this emphasis on engineering, improving the technical side of things. But, by March, 1940, the Radio Corporation of America felt it was necessary to forge ahead with its own plans, launched nearly a year before at the opening of the New York World's Fair. On the 20th of March, the Corporation began a big publicity campaign on television, leading off with full-page advertisements in the *New York Times* and the *New York Herald Tribune*.

The text revealed that RCA had cut the price of its receivers by about one-third, ". . . in anticipation of volume sales," so that "the average American family can well afford one." RCA announced plans to provide a regular television program service in the New York area. It offered sets to the public at moderate prices—$395 for the most expensive model, which included an all-wave radio. It reported the company was taking the initial step in constructing a television network.

Three days later, on March 23, 1940, the Federal Communications Commission ordered the Television Hearing reopened, stating:

Television promotional activities on the part of the Radio Corporation of America have prompted the Federal Communications Commission to order a further hearing, beginning April 8, to determine whether research and experimentation and the achievement of higher standards of television transmission are being unduly retarded by this company, its subsidiaries, or other licensees, and whether the effective date for the beginning of limited commercial operation should be changed from September 1 to some subsequent date. Meanwhile, that section of the new rules permitting restricted commercialization is suspended pending further order.

The current marketing campaign of the Radio Corporation of America is held to be at variance with the intent of the Commission's television report of February 29. Such action is construed as a disregard of the Commission's findings and recommendations for further improvement in the technique and quality of television transmission before sets are widely sold to the public.

The intent of the Commission was to give the industry further opportunity to move forward in an orderly manner and upon a sound scientific basis without causing injury to the public and resultant injury to the new industry itself, particularly to other manufacturers co-operating in seeking to bring about video improvements through experimentation rather than crowding the market with present-day receivers which may soon become obsolete. Economic loss to the public . . . would be occasioned by premature purchase in a rapidly advancing field.

Receiving sets constructed or on the market today may not be capable of receiving television programs from standardized television transmitters when the art has sufficiently advanced to permit such standardization. Public participation in television experimentation at this time is desirable only if the public understands that it is experimenting in reception and not necessarily investing in receiving equipment with a guarantee of its continued usefulness. Television is here to stay, but conceivably present-day receivers may for practical purposes be gone tomorrow.

Promotional activities directed to the sale of receivers not only intensifies the danger of these instruments being left on the hands of the public, but may react in the crystallizing of transmission standards at present levels. Moreover, the possibility of one manufacturer gaining an unfair advantage over competitors may cause them to abandon the further research and experimentation which is in the public interest and may result in crowding them into the market with apparatus at present efficiency levels. Rapid advance is desirable—but television is of great and permanent significance to the public. It is therefore of greater importance that the task be done thoroughly and with an eye to television's potential usefulness to the public. These are the goals which the Commission deems the public interest to require.

Said the newspapers, "The green light has been switched to red."

CHAPTER SIXTEEN

The Storm Before the Storm

THIS time television made headlines, front page ones. Controversy flared in newspapers and magazines— but a great deal of it was political in nature. A great deal of it seemed to omit any particular interest in the unsolved economic and technical problems, in favor of making the F. C. C. ruling a *cause célèbre* for a political reason. 1940 was, after all, the year of a national election, and columnists warmed over their old clichés about "bureaucracy," "usurpation of rights," and so on. While the politicians used television's problems as ammunition for their own cause, the television industry paused to take stock of the situation—and settle it.

Actually, it was a situation that was bound to arise sooner or later. In essence, it boiled down to this: Was television, as an industry and method of communication, something that could develop best under free, unrestricted, individualistic competition—*or* under a planned, technically standardized program, based on mutual scientific co-operation? Would the planned, restricted development of the past few years be continued —with the F. C. C. acting as the supervisor? Or would an individual company be able to forge ahead on its own as it saw fit?

Within the television industry itself opinions differed, naturally. David Sarnoff issued a statement denying any intentions of flouting the Commission's recommendations, and saying, "I am amazed at the action of the Commission. We have spent nearly $10,000,000 in developing television and in trying to create a new art and a new industry.

"We thought that we were proceeding exactly in accordance with the order on this subject recently adopted by the Commission."

The *New York Herald Tribune,* on March 26, 1940, wrote:

Allen B. Dumont,* president of the Dumont Laboratories, of Passaic, N. J., who is experimenting with 800-line transmission, said that "certain people" want to standardize television at 441 lines because it "fits into their patent situation." R.C.A., he said, had 441-line television patents tied up, whereas the patent situation above 441 was wide open.

The new television hearing, before the full Commission, began on April 8. Those who appeared and submitted evidence were, with few exceptions, the same representatives of the television industry who participated in the January hearing.

In the brief it submitted to the Commission the Philco Company pointed out that the F. C. C. clearly had the authority to fix transmission standards for television broadcasting. It stated also that if the Commission re-

---

* Correct spelling is Du Mont.

frained from exercising this authority, and if large numbers of receiving sets were sold to the public, the standards would become fixed "by a portion of the industry." The company's brief said, "The public outcry that would result from any later change in standards rendering receivers obsolete will effectively deprive the Commission of its statutory power."

On May 28, after the hearing was ended, the Commission issued a report, which included a review of previous Commission actions on television, an account of the April hearing, and its decision on television's immediate future.

The Commission felt that the intensive promotional campaign of RCA would tend toward the freezing of television broadcasting standards to the RCA system. Although regular program service by RCA's broadcasting subsidiary, NBC, was promoted and emphasized in extensive and varied public announcements, no mention was made of the experimental character of television broadcasting operations, or of the fact that only one television station was on the air in New York City, operating irregularly for two or three hours per day but not on all days of the week, or that future stations employing alternative systems of transmission might not be received by the sets offered for sale.

These factors were of concern to the F. C. C. not because of any question of fair trade practices, but because of their possible impact on television broadcasting standards.

The Commission's report also stated that the television industry, as a whole, did not agree with the RCA view of forging ahead with commercialization at that time "regardless of the untested possibilities of improvement on the horizon."

With this in mind, the Commission ruled:

. . . in order to assure to the public a television system which is the product of comparative research on known possibilities, standards of transmission should not now be set . . . there should be no commercial broadcasting with its deterring effects upon experimentation until such time as the probabilities of basic research have been fairly explored. . . . As soon as the engineering opinion of the industry is prepared to approve any one of the competing systems of broadcasting as the standard system, the Commission will consider the authorization of full commercialization.

The F. C. C. went on to say that when standards were approved, they "should afford within their limits reasonable flexibility for future advances in the science of television broadcasting." The Commission indicated it would grant experimental licenses in many parts of the country to stimulate experimentation and avoid concentrating television in a few large cities. But, to get a license, every station would have to do a substantial job of research. Available channels were strictly limited, and "they must be utilized in the public interest. The radio spectrum is public domain—development in television must be undertaken and advanced in order that this domain may be devoted to the best public use. There is no room for squatters. . . . Monopoly must be avoided." The Commission decided that no one company could operate more than three television stations.

Late in the summer of 1940, the inventor's front was heard from again—with something that might speed the development of television and hasten its acceptance by the public. For a good many years there had been isolated experiments with television in color. These experiments achieved some limited success in the laboratory but were completely unsuitable for regular broadcasting purposes. The television industry thought color might come eventually—that is, in twenty or thirty years. On August 29, 1940, a bombshell landed in the middle of the already snarled-up industry. The Columbia Broadcasting System announced that its Chief Engineer of Television, Peter Goldmark, had invented a practical, working system of color television. It was based on the experiments of Sir Isaac Newton, in 1666.

The industry was incredulous. Some of those companies holding patents on various phases of television were openly skeptical. Possibly they were afraid their methods would be made obsolete. Some seemed determined to discredit it, even though CBS was perfectly willing to let everyone make use of its new discovery.

Those who saw television in color, however, could not close their eyes to it. It worked. It was amazingly good—even in its earliest state of development. It was a major step forward. Paul Raibourn, Treasurer of Paramount Pictures and also of Du Mont Television, praised it as a significant advance. Gerald Cock, United States representative of the British Broadcasting Corporation, termed it "astounding" and "a miracle," stating that if television had been launched in color, it would have already become a universal medium of entertainment and instruction.

By the spring of 1941, all the fundamental problems of research had been solved, and CBS had made complete information on its color process available to the rest of the industry upon request. The use of its patents was not restricted, and Chairman Fly of the F.C.C. urged the other television companies to take advantage of the opportunity and hasten the introduction of broadcasting in color. The next step was to begin a test period of experimental transmissions in color, which could have been completed in six months if the entire television industry had been willing to co-operate. This was what the F.C.C. urged in its report of May 3, 1941, suggesting that the other broadcasters test color for six months and report back to the F.C.C. with the results. For one reason or another, the other companies did nothing about it, and CBS entered the only report on color at the beginning of 1942. It was based on the results of experimental color transmissions held every week-day afternoon. Faced by this unfortunate apathy and studious preoccupation with other problems plus the acute shortage of technicians and materials, CBS was forced to discontinue its color experiments for the duration of the war.

During the winter of 1940-1, the F.C.C. had carefully studied the latest engineering developments in the country. Discussions and hearings by representatives of the television industry before the Commission revealed that, at last, there was more or less universal agreement as to just what the transmission standards should be. A voluntary association of all television companies proposed standards which the F.C.C. adopted, for black and white television—525 lines of definition and thirty complete pictures a second. An improved form of "synchronization" was adopted to keep pictures "in frame" even under bad static conditions. Any future changes would be made only if it were "in the public interest, convenience, and necessity," and the date of any possible change would be determined in the light of its effect on the obsolescence of receivers in the homes of the public.

These standards were officially adopted in the report dated May 3, 1941, which also announced that television was to go on a full "commercial" basis beginning on July 1, 1941. Sponsored programs were to be permitted. This, however, was more or less "academic," to quote Adrian Murphy, then head of CBS Television. The number of television receivers available was so small—only about 5,000 were then in use in the New York area—that any advertising rates must be very small. (Rates are based, in part, on the number of sets in any given market.)

Furthermore, these receivers would not be able to pick up programs until they were remodeled to accommodate for:

(a) Raising of picture from 441 lines to 525.

(b) All sound being broadcast by FM—necessitating a change of all sound transmitters and sound receivers, which had operated previously on "Amplitude Modulation."

(c) The television broadcasting channels being shifted.

The lowest channel—44 to 50 megacycles—had been taken from television and allotted to FM broadcasting. Therefore, most television stations shifted to new channels. This meant their transmitters must be rebuilt—a job which in some cases took three months and cost the better part of $100,000. These transmitters had been designed to operate on one particular channel, and the equipment could not always function as efficiently on a different frequency. But—since there was a war going and priorities were in effect, it was not always possible to get new equipment. The broadcasters scratched their heads.

Still another complication existed beyond that—in the public's receiving sets, which also had to be rebuilt. The set manufacturers offered to do this free of charge, saddling themselves with the cost. To get all the sets back to the factory and remodel them was a long and costly job.

Previously, there had been a gap left between the frequencies of channels 2 and 3. It had been used for experimental work by the Government. Many television receivers had been so built that they could not receive *anything* in that gap. They did not have any "innards" to fit the wave-length. When the fellows on old channel 2 moved up one step, they slid out into thin air where practically no one could pick them up—until new equipment was built and installed in receivers. This was the situation in which the New York CBS station, WCBW found itself. When WCBW went on the air July 1st, 1941, it was broadcasting its programs to "the little man who wasn't there."

The formal date for the beginning of "commercial" television had arrived, but actually it did not mean very much. It was more a promise for the future than the sudden blossoming of a new era. Not only was the audience small, but there were very few television receivers available and no increase in the supply was likely.

The immediate future of public television broadcasting was most uncertain and faced the possibility of curtailment or outright suspension. For one thing, the demands of war production had produced a great shortage of certain raw materials and manufactured equipment necessary to keep a television station going. Unless television broadcasting could contribute something of value to the war effort, it might be unable to get enough tubes, wires, and whatnots to stay on the air—literally. Beyond that, the highly trained technicians needed to operate and maintain television equipment were scarce, *and* were needed to design, build, and operate equipment used by the Army and Navy. Engineers were being removed from television broadcasting and put into the armed services—creating a shortage in the studios and transmitters which reached a critical point.

Beyond that, with the audience for television programs comparatively small and no new sets being made available to the public, the broadcasters might not be able to continue the expenditures necessary to put on television programs. When you are spending between $10,000. and $15,000. a week for programs—and it is all outgo, with nothing coming in and nothing likely to come in for an indefinite number of years—it does become a bit of a drain on the exchequer!

Nevertheless, the programs went on steadily, improving all the time. Experiments in different types were carried out as much as was possible under the existing circumstances. Although most broadcasting activity was fostered by the radio networks, television was pretty much on its own. Radio programs, as such, are not suitable for television. The techniques are very different, for radio is meant to be heard but not seen. A radio program, when it is seen, usually loses most of its intended effect. To be sure, television could adapt certain aspects of radio practice, as well as movie and theater practice. In the main, however, it had to build its own techniques and stand on its own legs. In essence, it is a new and different art form—and it must develop as such.

During 1941 and 1942, the public as a whole was unaware of the existence of television, and the press seemed uninclined to give it any publicity—the premature publicity blasts of the past decade having made it seem like something from the land of "never never." The television broadcasters themselves, realizing that the great period of expansion would come only after the war was over, did not make any great efforts to publicize it. That is, no high-pressure attempt was made to build it to great proportions. This was in keeping with the policy agreed upon by the F.C.C. and the industry. Publicity of a conservative, "institutional" class was welcomed if it came along—the aim being to build a good name, a solid foundation, and to remove the "never never" stigma.

Inevitably the cry was raised that someone was holding television down for selfish reasons. Possibly this was true in some isolated cases, but it would have been awfully hard to prove. In a capitalistic society, and under the American system of broadcasting, there could be no other course. The only way to push television to its *fullest* extent in 1940-1941, the only way to have put it on a "big business basis," would have been to scrap the American way of broadcasting and socialize it. And that idea would not exactly have pleased the American public, or the private broadcasters.

Despite the obstacles, the F.C.C. was doing all it could to further the development of television. With a similar objective in view the American Television Society was organized in the late summer of 1941. Composed of television enthusiasts in various fields, the Society set out to foster the embryonic art in every possible way, particularly as a valuable adjunct to the country's war effort, or national defense effort as it was called in 1941. Late in October, the Society's President, Norman D. Waters—also head of the advertising agency bearing his name—made a trip to Washington to confer with government officials on the linking of television with national defense. On his return he reported that the F.C.C. was studying the situation in detail and would soon take action to speed its growth.

The television broadcasting stations were already presenting shows on current events, news, and national defense, but these programs were largely done by the individual studios. It was difficult to get any considerable assistance from government agencies, which already had their hands full with radio, movies, and press. (All of which had mass audiences, whereas the New York television audience, in the fall of 1941, was probably less than 50,000 people.) Nevertheless, programs about the armed services and war industries were rounded up. The first regular, visualized news schedule was an afternoon and evening feature of WCBW, in New York, stressing the world-wide aspects of the war by an ingenious use of dozens of graphic, pictorialized maps.

The autumn months of 1941 passed, and December

was at hand. Sunday the 7th . . . Pearl Harbor . . . and the war had spread around the earth. The United States went on a "total war" basis. What was going to happen to television in a country at war? What part did it play in the war effort? What had happened to it in a world at war, in Europe, in Asia?

We have traced the growth of television since the introduction of the iconoscope, in 1933, in the United States alone. To round out our picture, let us take a glance at what happened to television after 1933 in Asia, in Europe, in more than a dozen countries. Then we can complete the picture of television at war, on the home front, and on the military front.

CHAPTER SEVENTEEN

The London Palace

ON September 1, 1939, the Nazi horde began to overrun Poland, and the war exploded throughout Europe. On that day, even before Britain had declared war on Germany, English television became the first casualty of World War II in the British Isles. On that day, September 1, was abruptly ended the first high quality public television service the world had ever seen. The British Broadcasting Corporation, in the years between 1935 and the outbreak of war, had taken the lead in television broadcasting.

The story of BBC Television had begun in 1929, when the Corporation decided to assist the Baird Television Company in its television experiments. Facilities for experimental "low-definition" vision transmissions were provided—using thirty lines of definition and twelve and one half pictures per second. These experiments were to be broadcast through the medium-wave London station transmitter in Oxford Street, London. The test broadcasts were continued in 1930 from the new London regional station at Brookmans Park. In

1930 sound was broadcast along with the pictures. Two years later, the BBC equipped a studio in Broadcasting House with Baird Apparatus.

Looking back at the television scene in 1933 it now seems almost as fantastic as a scene from a movie by H. G. Wells. The background scenery was a sheet of dead white, and the floor was broken up into alternate black and white squares—like a chess board. The faces of the performers were grotesquely made up in black and white. Lips and eyebrows were dead black, while the skin was a pure white. And since two widely separated wave lengths were necessary to transmit these programs—one wave length for sound and one for vision—it meant that television test programs had to be given at times when they did not interfere with the regular radio programs. As a result, the transmissions usually took place between 11 P.M. and midnight.

With the rapid development of cathode ray tube cameras in 1933 the BBC began to consider the possibilities of offering a public television service of high quality. In May 1934, the Postmaster General appointed a committee to investigate the situation. In a report, issued in January, 1935, the Committee recommended that the British Broadcasting Corporation should be responsible for television, and a high-definition service should be established at an early date. The first station was to be in London, and two different companies were to try out their systems on alternate weeks. The cost of television was to be borne by the revenue obtained from the existing government license fee of ten shillings on every radio receiver.

These recommendations were accepted by the Government, and Alexandra Palace was chosen as the site of the station. It is fairly near the center of London, located on one of the highest points of ground available—some 300 feet above sea level. The southeastern tower of the Palace was chopped off about 80 feet above the ground and heavily reinforced. Then a 220-foot mast of steel lattice work was erected upon it, with the antennae at the top —some 600 feet above sea level.

The two competing companies were Baird and Marconi-E.M.I. Marconi-E.M.I. used a camera called the "Emitron," which was based on Zworykin's iconoscope. Baird was testing two different methods. One was the "intermediate film" process. In this method a motion picture film was taken on the program in progress. After being developed in approximately 65 seconds, it was run through the front of a teleciné camera using a rotating, Nipkow disk. Baird's other method used his "Electron Camera," based largely on Philo Farnsworth's "image dissector" patents. On one week Marconi-E.M.I. would broadcast with their method. The next week it would be Baird, with one of his methods.

The Alexandra Palace station was formally opened on November 2, 1936. Two hours of programs were broadcast every day, at 3:00 and 9:00 P.M. In February 1937, as the result of the experience gained by the transmissions of both systems from Alexandra Palace, the Television Advisory Committee recommended that the experimental period be ended and a single set of standards be adopted for all transmissions in the future. These standards were known as the London Television Standards, and were those employed in the Marconi-E.M.I. system. It was announced that these standards, 405 lines of definitions, with interlaced scanning and 25 *complete* pictures a second, would remain fixed for at least three years.

The occasion of the first anniversary of public television in England was celebrated in the London newspapers, and the growing pains in the "London Palace of magic" were featured in a long article in the *London Times,* on January 7, 1938, which said in part:

The official anniversary of public television came on November 2, 1937, but in the eyes of the staff of 265 at the Alexandra Palace the significant date is February 5 of this year. Twelve months will then have passed since the Television Advisory Committee approved the superiority of the Marconi-E.M.I. to the Baird system, and the single standard of transmission was established. Up to that point lack of space and time had severely hampered the efforts to transform television for the private viewer from an ingenious toy into a serious entertainment.

Television is incongruously housed. Gaunt and unlovely, the Palace dominates part of North London, with only the 220-foot mast to indicate the marvel in the south-east corner. An inadvertent entry by the back door brings the visitor over a desolate branch terminus of the L.N.E.R. into empty, echoing halls, where the assorted objects might have been gathered by a surrealist. Sections of stuffed lions, slot-machines, a bar, posters of dance competitions, and a statue of Lincoln are distributed haphazard. Only a discreet grey door in a corner, painted "No Entry," marks the back entrance to the overcrowded hive of television. Here the essentials are in the vision and sound transmitting halls on the ground floor, and in two studios above them, one of which is a second string formerly used for the Baird system. On the other side of a narrow corridor, which is both artery and boulevard, are the make-up and dressing rooms, and on the ground floor is a small restaurant. The executive staff's rooms are in the east tower, and in the north-west corner of the building, separated from the rest by the Winter Garden, is the carpenter's shop and an old theatre which the station has acquired with an open mind for whatever purpose it may be needed.

The station's day has two feverish campaigns, culminating at 3 o'clock in the afternoon and 9 o'clock in the evening. Peele's cry from the heart, "O Time too swift, O swiftness never ceasing" would be the best inscription for the doorway. For example, the piano-tuner has to arrive at 7 A.M., because there is no room for him later. The morning is filled with rehearsals and a film demonstration for the benefit of the radio trade, and rehearsals have to be juggled in and out of the two stages. This is where the producers, the best and most successful of whom come from the stage, are most harassed. For the convenience of artists, early rehearsals take place at Broadcasting House or Maida Vale; if the artists came to the station more frequently they might find no space to rehearse in. When a condensed Othello was performed recently there was only one two-hour rehearsal on the stage. Three-quarters of an hour were spent in setting it, the positions of the players being defined by yellow chalk marks on the white linoleum. This left an hour and a quarter for actual camera rehearsal of a play which was going to take an hour to perform. The actress who played Desdemona had never seen a television camera before, so that she had little enough time to learn how to act into the camera or to master the art of two-dimensional gesture. . . .

Such difficulties are due to limitations of space and money inevitable at this point in the development of television, but their existence tends to create a controlled frenzy towards zero hour. At 2:55 P.M or 8:55 P.M. the principal stage is set. The lights are fixed and three to four cameras and two to three microphones are in position, with the cameramen wearing earphones so as to be in touch with the producer in his control tower above the stage.

The producer is the linchpin of every item, and his control tower, separated from the stage by darkened plate glass, is the most significant place in the studio, for it shows the technical complexities and the difference between television and other forms of entertainment—stage, screen, or sound broadcasting.

The producer sits next the window, looking at two frames. One frame shows the image in course of transmission; on to the other he can switch the field of vision of any camera on the set. Beside him sits the production manager, whose functions are similar to those of a stage manager in a theatre (the stage manager of television is on the set taking notes). In front of the producer sit the sound engineer controlling total output, and the sound mixer selecting and cutting it. Behind him is the key man, the vision-mixer. The platform also holds the senior engineer as a roving wing forward, another man in charge of the gramophone, and a junior engineer logging the programme.

This means that there is a team of eight handling the performance between the moment of recording and the moment of transmission to the viewer. Four of the eight—producer, sound engineer, and sound and vision mixers—are indispensable. Nor do they have much time to relax at 4 p.m., when the afternoon programme ends, because rehearsal, experiment, and audition start again and so on into the evening. Up to now the record of hurried achievement is held by the clergyman from Tristan da Cunha, who appeared in an evening version of "Picture Page". . . . He was held up by fog and traffic, and reaching the Palace five minutes before the programme finished was hurried straight on to the stage, unrehearsed, to explain his island.

It might be inferred that this running fight with the clock would mean nerves and discontent. Producers and artists would like many more rehearsals, and the engineering staff might prefer not to work right through both programmes on alternate days. But the cheerfulness of the staff, from which there have been only two secessions since the service started, is a contribution to industrial psychology proving the value to the individual of work in a small undertaking. The glossy impersonality of Broadcasting House has not yet descended on television. Where everyone knows everyone else, generally by Christian or nick-names, and where an executive department consists of one man and a secretary, correct deportment and the circulation of memoranda are superfluous; continual personal contact oils the machinery. Nor, even if the organization were bigger, would it be easy to clap the staff into their pigeon-holes, when so many jobs call for the all-rounder. On one side the executives and producers must have a quota of technical knowledge, and on the other, the cameraman and the vision-mixer must have more artistic sense than can be given by previous instruction.

The prevalent spirit was expressed by the studio hand who said, "We're not working; we're being paid for a hobby."

The London television service continued to expand and improve through 1938, and although the sale of tele-vision sets to the public was not as rapid as might have been hoped for, nevertheless sets were selling. This despite the fact that prices were high, for sets were not in mass production yet. Most of the television re-ceivers on sale employed cathode ray tubes for picture reproduction—at least 75 per cent of the sets on the market. The other 25 per cent employed a mechanical system, using mirror drums. It was possible to get a tele-vision receiver with a screen giving a picture 14 inches by 11 inches in size plus an all-wave radio receiver, for between 70 and 80 guineas. This picture was larger in size than those available in the first years of American television broadcasting—three years later. It was possible to get receivers equipped with large screen projection type cathode ray tubes, or large screen mechanical re-ceivers, for a cost of around 150 to 200 guineas. The high price of these large screen receivers (the equivalent of $750 to $1,000) meant that they were available only to people of ample means or to those who wished to show television simultaneously to large numbers of view-ers. But, in the first years of American broadcasting no large screen receivers of the projection type were available to the public.

By the second anniversary of the public service, in November 1938, it was estimated that the BBC had spent a total of $4,000,000 in two years of operation. About this time, plans began to get under way to extend the television service beyond the London area, to the large cities such as Manchester.

In 1939 the television programs reached a high degree of excellence. In May, when the television audience was asked, in mailed questionnaires, its opinion of the programs being broadcast, the replies were 90 per cent favorable.

Large screen projectors had been installed in London theaters, and in July it was announced that the Baird Television Company was putting large screen receivers in three additional London theaters, doubling the number of movie houses with Baird Television installations. The Scophony Company was also installing screens in theaters.

But the days of British television were numbered. Let Ernest C. Thomson,* of the BBC television studio, tell you how it happened:

At noon on 1 September 1939, the television announcer at the radio exhibition at Olympia wound up the morning transmission with a light-hearted recital of good things to come. Next week the lucky owners of television sets were to have a fine feast: five full-length plays, solo acts by at least two stars of the first magnitude, two new editions of "Picture Page," outside broadcasts, films, and much else besides.

But up at Alexandra Palace a few people who watched the screen from the Central Control Room were sadly shaking

* From *BBC Handbook*, 1940.

their heads. The telephone message which they had been dreading for days had not yet come, but now it could only be a matter of minutes.

It was decided to keep the station on the air a little longer. The announcer's farewell smile faded into a riotous cartoon film—"Mickey's Gala Premiere"—which ran for 8 minutes and finished when a caricatured Garbo sighed: "Ah tank ah go home." Those were the last words transmitted from the television station. The close-down order came at 12:10. Undramatically, without even a closing announcement, the world's first high-definition television service was halted on the threshold of certain success.

When the service closed down, there were already more than 20,000 viewers, compared with half that number a year before. But the increase which was believed to be imminent last September would probably have been out of all proportion to the previous rise, for reports from Radiolympia at the end of August showed that at last television really had "caught on." The ordinary man was beginning to realize that he could have it in his home for a few shillings a week. . . .

To talk of the television programmes during those last eight months of the service is to stir wistful memories. We throw a glance nowadays at the blank screens of our receivers and remember when they held us like a spell. We recall the constantly changing scene: Royal processions, tennis at Wimbledon, comedies and thrillers in the studios, the big fights at Harringay and Earl's Court, the living portraits of "Picture Page," the breath-catching tumbling acts of variety, the fun and music of revue and cabaret, the pure pictorial beauty of masque and opera, and we ask with Keats, "Was it a vision, or a waking dream?"

Britain's television was postponed for the duration—by military necessity. In February, 1940, the Postmaster was questioned in the House of Commons about the possibilities of resuming television broadcasting as an encouragement both to research work and to manufacture television sets, enabling them to establish a British product in world markets. The Postmaster General replied that he could hold out no hope of an early resumption of the television service. Despite his expressed opinion, agitation continued in the trade and in the public press for a resumption of the programs. Then, in the spring of 1940, the German blitzkrieg began and France fell. All further thoughts of resuming the television service before a victorious conclusion of the war were dropped.

Public broadcasting was not to be resumed, but television research went on—because of the value of its application as a weapon of war. John L. Baird was continuing his study of stereoscopic television, to give a three-dimensional effect. At the same time he was also working on his ideas for color television. Both these lines of research went back to his early experiments in the 1920's. British television interests were not going to be outstripped as British film interests were at the end of the First World War. At that time American motion picture interests had cornered the world market, and British films were unable to re-establish themselves, on a worldwide basis, until after 1930. British television pioneers, as they pushed their research during World War II, also hoped to strengthen their financial position so they would be able to meet the certain challenge of American television companies at the end of the Second World War.

England would be ready to take its place as one of the leaders in postwar television development.

CHAPTER EIGHTEEN

Casualties

THE progress of the British television service was pretty generally known in the late 1930's. What was not so commonly known was the spread of television all over the world.

The new cathode ray tube cameras had opened new fields. Television began to sprout from New York to Argentina to Russia to Iceland. In 1938, plans were afoot to build a television transmitter on the highest point of ground in Reykjavik, the capital of Iceland. The United States Commercial Attaché in Copenhagen reported that the Danish government hoped to conduct television experiments in Iceland, even though the total radio audience there was only about 14,000 people.

In Holland the development of television was largely in the hands of the Philips Company. Late in 1935, engineers of this international radio and electrical company built the first iconoscope in Europe. They began experimental transmissions with pictures of 180-line definition, 25 frames per second. Later the quality of the picture was stepped up to about 450 lines. This work was under the general direction of G. Holst, with Balth. van der Pol specializing in theoretical development, and J. van der Mark on the practical application of matters.

In 1938, the Philips Company constructed a portable transmitter, equipped with iconoscopes, and demonstrated television throughout Holland and a number of other European countries—to show what electronic television was like. In this tour the Philips engineers transmitted pictures of 405-line definition—the British standard. On occasion, the definition could be raised to 567 lines. During this same period, the Philips Company also developed the high-pressure mercury vapor lamp. This type of light—used in some American television studios —is manufactured in the United States by General Electric, under Philips patents. It gives off a very intense bluish-white light. To eliminate all heat, the lamp is cooled by a circulating water system, making it perfectly comfortable for those who work in its light.

In Holland, the actual radio broadcasting was done by two large stations. These stations were privately run but did not maintain themselves by advertising, as American radio does. Neither were they supported by the government. Each was entirely maintained by voluntary contributions from large numbers of people. Government control came in the form of a license to operate, issued by the Postal Department.

The Philips Company, manufacturer of most radio equipment in Holland, did not itself engage in any broadcasting—save for experimental operations to test apparatus, radio and television.

In 1939, everything was set for a new spurt of activity. The two large radio stations had applied for permission to engage in television broadcasting. The Netherlands government had appointed a commission, which had investigated the field and the available equipment of the radio stations. It had also visited the Philips laboratories, which had manufactured equipment to operate on both the French and the British standards.

The Philips receiving sets also had been developed to a point of considerable excellence. (For the British market receivers were available with large screen projection tubes.) For the home, Philips offered a set with a picture screen of 14½ by 18 inches. It included an all-wave high fidelity sound radio and sold for 120 guineas. New equipment was being prepared in anticipation of the Radio Olympia Exhibit, scheduled for the autumn of 1939 in London.

Then war broke out and the television plans of the Dutch companies were postponed. Less than a year later, Holland was overrun by the Nazis.

In France, experimental television broadcasts had been maintained in 1932 and 1933 by the Television Baird-Nathan Company, an affiliate of the John L. Baird Company. These tests, using a mechanical scanning system, were continued through 1935. In April of that year the transmission standards were raised to 60 lines of definition in the picture. On November 17, 1935 a new station was opened with a one kilowatt transmitter in the Eiffel Tower. The antenna was at the top of the tower, and the studio was located two and a half kilometers away at 103 Rue de Grenelle, connected to the transmitter by a coaxial cable. When this new station was opened, the mechanical scanning system was improved to 180 lines of definition, using a cumbersome camera mounted on four small wheels, hardly suitable for flexible manipulation about a studio.

In 1937, the French Administration des Postes, Télégraphes et Téléphones improved the Paris television station for the Paris Exhibition. A new set of apparatus employing an iconoscope was installed, giving 441-line definition. Visitors to the Paris Exhibition had the opportunity of seeing television broadcasts every afternoon and evening. Sidewalk interviews of passers-by were conducted in much the same way that they were at the New York World's Fair two years later.

In April of the following year, with an eye to constructing a television network, a special cable was laid joining Paris with Bordeaux, passing by Limoges and branching off to Brize-Toulouse. About the same time a new transmitter was put into operation in the Eiffel Tower. It had a peak power of 25,000 watts, which subsequently was reported as raised to 30,000 watts in the summer of 1938. In the summer of 1939 it was reported that it had a normal power of 30,000 watts, with a top capacity of 45,000 watts. This would have made it the most powerful television transmitter in regular operation in the world at that time. At the same time the picture quality was improved to 455 lines of definition. Observers reported that pictures of exceptional quality and precision were picked up throughout the service area, which extended for a radius of 20 or 25 miles around Paris. Although the pictures from the high-power transmitter are reported to have been better in technical quality than those obtained in Germany, the entertainment value of the programs appears to have been far below those put out in London.

Plans for the continuation of public television became uncertain with the outbreak of war, although it was reported that the French army was experimenting with television for the observation of artillery fire by airplane. Then, in the summer of 1940, television in France became another war casualty and all its physical materials were taken over by the Nazis.

In Sweden, television demonstrations were given around 1930 by the John L. Baird Company—demonstrating in the Röda Kvarn movie theater in Stockholm. These demonstrations were not widely viewed, and were not broadcast through the air—the transmitter and receiver were connected by cable. Until about 1935 or 1936 television was considered more or less as a plaything for engineers. All the development in Sweden was done by private engineering concerns, although it was necessarily licensed by the Swedish Board of Telegraphy. In 1935 a television transmitter was erected in Stockholm by the Svenska Radio A.B., a subsidiary of the L. M. Ericsson Telephone Manufacturing Company and largest radio concern in Sweden. A German concern, Loewe, assisted in the design and construction of the transmitter, which was carried on under the direction of Gunnar Hok. During the first few months he used a picture with 180 lines of definition, which was later raised to 240 lines with twenty-five pictures a second. The purpose of this experiment was to make the public acquainted with television through public demonstration. A regular daily schedule was kept for a short time during the Christmas shopping season of 1935. A number of cathode ray receivers were placed at strategic spots in Stockholm—such as department stores, moving picture theaters, and newspaper offices. The transmitter was equipped only with a mechanical film scanner. There were no direct pick-ups of live subjects at that time.

In 1938, the Philips Company of Holland held a television demonstration for several weeks. These demonstrations were on a commercial basis, and a large part of the population of Stockholm turned out to see the program. The demonstrations by the Philips Company brought television much closer to the Swedish public.

The Swedish Board of Telegraphy—Kungliga Telegraffstyrelsen—was said to have been considering the question of television at that time, and it officially announced that television broadcasting would be inaugurated in Sweden as soon as possible. However, the economic difficulties were such that it seemed a bit remote. However, engineers were being trained in the Kungliga Tekniska Hogskolen under Professor Erik Lövgren, one of the leading Scandinavian experts on video and high frequency circuits.

All this took place before the outbreak of war. When the war spread all around Sweden the prospect of television before the end of hostilities was definitely out.

Television was a war casualty in Poland, too. As far back as January, 1937, the United States Commercial Attaché in Warsaw had reported that the Polish Radio Company and the State Institute for Telecommunications were planning an experimental station in Warsaw. For this purpose they had leased the roof of the Prudential Building, which was the highest in Warsaw. It was planned that the television station would be installed on the roof of this building, and plans were made to erect a tower and broadcasting mast 26 meters high. A Nazi propaganda photo, appearing in a New York newspaper in 1942, showed this building completely gutted.

In Russia, in the mid 1930's, television experimentation was carried on using low definition mechanical systems. The quality of these pictures was raised 240 lines of definition in 1936, and at that time work was begun on the construction of a television center in Moscow. This was equipped with American apparatus, ordered from the Radio Corporation of America. Shortly before war broke out in 1939, Charles K. Freeman, the American stage director, visited the Moscow television studio and he described this visit in an article for *Variety*. Mr. Freeman wrote:

Russia is a country of contradictions, in the field of sight and sound vibrations, no less than diplomacy. They have been at television a little over a year now and have yanked apart and put together RCA cameras and transmitters, fooled around with lights, acoustics, and telecinema apparatus to see how they all work, and how speedily they can make duplications.

Not only will the Russian stop in the middle of his work to discuss what's going on in kindred fields elsewhere, he'll take you (once you get inside) around his home-made plant, and insist that you see cameras, transmitters, programs, even the ventilating system. I saw them all and spent considerable time with program director Bolchakof and Engineer Shaperovsky at the Moscow plant. They aren't up to any of the Westerners as yet, but they are covering ground.

Television is very new in Russia. The Soviet imported some RCA 1937 equipment and started experiments with film and concert programs. There are few privately "owned" sets. Instead receivers were being set up in club rooms and social halls. These have been getting one program a day for two hours' duration.

Programs are a combination of film, concert and dramatic entertainment with visiting scientists and Soviet bigwigs being propped on occasion in front of the iconoscope. I witnessed, among others, an impressive array of talent from the Vachtangov theatre in four vignettes of that theatre's repertoire. Among the players was the late Boris Shukin, who became famous for his portrayal of Lenin and who was, up to his recent untimely death, one of the most gifted artists in the Soviet Union. Since the talent field is state-controlled there is no limit to the extent of able people at the beck and call of the program directors.

Accustomed . . . to perfect studio acoustics and "dead" sound, one is amazed at the appearance of hardwood floors and wood panels in the Moscow studio. . . . Sound interference is due also to the lack of sufficient incandescent lighting, though arc lamps now being used for studio programs are fast being replaced. The producers are likewise hampered by the scarcity of cameras. A pretty tricky dramatic show I watched was covered with but one unit, dollying, panning and moving in for close-ups with facility. All equipment is now being manufactured in Leningrad where the one other station is located, and I was assured that the next visit I made would find them well equipped.

I was told that Leningrad's engineer Braude has worked out a new system of cinema transmission and is working on a new device that will replace the present iconoscope. The Moscow station has a tower 150 meters high and diffusion regularly around 30 kilometers, with a record reception gained of 70 kilometers. There is a splendid control room modeled after RCA specifications. . . .

The Russians are eager to perfect television since the stage, radio and cinema are strong arms of the government propaganda division. They have the same excited interest in engineering problems as a youngster presented with a new Erector set, and since rubles are plentiful and space unconfining they may . . . contribute something substantial to the television scene.

Great developments were planned by the Soviet Union for a television station and projects were under way in Moscow, in Leningrad, and in Kiev. In 1940 a large number of television receivers were under construction, and several scientific research institutes were engaged on the problem of rendering television as widespread and accessible to the Russian public as was sound radio. The great new television center was planned in the projected Palace of Soviets. It was planned that the Palace would have up to fifty broadcasting points in the building and in adjacent squares. A new broadcasting mast was planned to go on top of the building, which would be 975 feet high. It was expected that the broadcasting mast would be visible as far as 62 miles away from Moscow. Large screen installations were planned in the building—with pictures ranging in size from one-half a meter square up to 100 square meters—this large size to be installed in the grand hall of the Palace, which was to seat 21,000 people.

The plans were all made. The foundations of the building had been laid when the war intervened, and a blanket of silence dropped over all television operations. Presumably the television activity ceased with the outbreak of war, and journalists in Moscow in 1941 reported that they did not see or hear of any television activity.

Stories of impending television activity in other widely scattered parts of the world appeared in the late 1930's.

All of these were indefinitely postponed after the outbreak of war. A small television company—in connection with an American concern, The International Television Radio Corporation, was set up in Australia in 1938. Apparently nothing ever came of it.

There has been television experimentation in Argentina, using cathode ray tube apparatus. In the spring of 1939 a traveling show of German television cameras and receivers was demonstrated at the Buenos Aires postal conference. The Prime Minister of Argentina was among those present at the first demonstration by the enterprising Nazi concern. The traveling demonstration, run by picked men of the German Post Office staff, then went to Rio de Janeiro for three weeks and then to Guatemala and Chile. In 1941 it was rumored that the owner of a large Buenos Aires radio station was negotiating with an American concern to purchase television equipment in order to set up a station in Argentina.

At the other end of the Western Hemisphere, in Canada, television experimentation was going on in laboratories at Toronto and Montreal, but, because of the great financial problems involved, the official policy of the Canadian Broadcasting Corporation was to wait and see how television made out in the United States and England. Then, when it was more fully developed there, the Canadian Broadcasting Corporation planned to enter the television field.

To round out our picture of how television began to sprout around the world, only to become a casualty in World War II, we need to look at three more countries. The next chapter touches briefly on what happened to television in Japan, Italy, and particularly in Germany.

CHAPTER NINETEEN

Berlin—Rome—Tokyo

ON April 20, 1935, the *New York Sun* carried a little article which read:

Extremely jealous of their leadership (sic) in television developments are the Germans, who claim the "right of being the premier country in television belongs to Germany," because of ultra-short wave tests that have been conducted in Berlin for several years. Plans for Germany's television service, shortly to be opened to the public, includes the erection of twenty-five ultra-short wave transmitters throughout the country.

On April 27, the *Sun* ran another story, announcing that the Farnsworth Television Corporation, of Philadelphia, had signed agreements with a German company, Fernseh, A. G., for a complete interchange of patents. Fernseh announced that its mechanical scanning disk methods would be replaced by the Farnsworth image dissector tube. (Under Hitler, the two big German television manufacturing companies were Telefunken and Fernseh, A. G. The word *Fernseh* is adapted from the German word for television—*fern,* meaning distant, and

sehen, to see. According to John L. Baird, the Fernseh
company was formed in 1929, as a combination of the
Baird Company, the Zeiss Ikon Optical Company, the
Bosch Magneto Company, and the Loewe Radio Company, for the purpose of developing the Baird mechanical television system in Germany.

The same day, April 27, 1935, the Associated Press
filed a dispatch from Berlin, saying: "The Nazi government hopes to use television widely to cement further its
grip on Germany, a grip whose strength is the huge
propaganda machinery, with the powerful German
broadcasting system as one of its main instruments."

The *London Daily Telegraph,* on August 9, 1935, carried a dispatch from its Berlin correspondent who wrote
that German television had been put in the hands of
Hermann Goering, Reichsminister for Aviation. Previously, it had been under the control of Propaganda
Minister Dr. Paul Goebbels. On July 12, Goering had
stressed that television was of "special importance in
respect of the safety of aircraft, and the protection of
the (German) nation in the air." The *Daily Telegraph*
correspondent speculated on the possibility that Nazi
planes were then being equipped with television apparatus. This was the summer of 1935, and television became a part of the German air force. Technical development went ahead under forced draught, for the power of
television as a weapon—in propaganda and in military
uses—was recognized.

Its propaganda usage became apparent first.

What was claimed to be the world's longest television
cable came into operation in September, 1937, for the
German Post Office's regular television-telephone service

between Berlin and Nuremberg, and for direct-vision relays of the Party Rally from the Witzleben television station.

At that time the price of a television-telephone "see and talk" was RM. 4.20 for three minutes, just double the price of an ordinary trunk call over the same distance. The service was limited to the two television-telephone offices in Berlin and to the one in Nuremberg, the cable being capable of handling only two 180-line pictures for the television-telephone. The actual cable had been designed, however, for the band required for the 441-line pictures of television broadcasting.

Wrote one Berlin correspondent:*

The German Post Office authorities granted me facilities to speak with Nuremberg on two occasions on the opening day. In the one case I conversed with, and saw, a man whom I think I shall recognize again if ever I meet him in Berlin. Later I had a "talk and see" with an English friend who asked me to read the paper he was holding up. This was not quite possible, although one recognized the characters, and occasional words, in the headlines. The picture gives a full head-and-collar image. . . .

But it is only when watching Nuremberg street scenes, in a Berlin television room, that one realizes the real achievement of the cable. Here I was just off a busy Berlin thoroughfare, watching Herr Hitler drive up to his hotel, walk out on to the balcony and salute the people in Nuremberg, over three hundred miles away. Unfortunately for the Post Office, the engineers did not seem in tune with their apparatus. Their "sidechat," which was partly audible, made us realize that, and results were poor. They will undoubtedly improve as the relays continue; but the people in my television room were greatly disappointed when the picture deteriorated just at

* Of the BBC publication, *World-Radio*.

the moment the Führer appeared on the balcony, especially as, a few minutes before, the very helmets of the police among the crowd had been clearly recognizable.

During the Party Rally, Berlin's eleven and Potsdam's one television rooms will be open from 10:00-12:00 and 4:00-6:00, in addition to the evening session from 8:00 to 10:00. The morning and afternoon programmes will be largely devoted to direct-vision relays from Nuremberg.

The German Post Office employed mechanical scanning apparatus, giving 180-line definition, for their two-way television-telephone service, which was soon extended from Berlin, over Leipzig, to Nuremberg and Munich, a distance of roughly 410 miles.

In 1938, the German public—"Aryan" only—was allowed to use this service by going to a public station, a *Fernsehsprechstelle*.* In Berlin there were two: one in Kolumbus Haus on Potsdamerplatz, the other in west Berlin, on the corner of Hardenberg and Kantstrasse. Similar *Fernsehsprechstellen* were located in the other cities on the line—Leipzig, Nuremberg, and Munich.

The Nazi government presented its television to the world with shrewd showmanship, making it look better than probably it was. Technically, with the possible exception of the design of receivers, the consensus of opinion among informed observers is that England and Germany produced a picture of about equal quality. However, England had a regular broadcast service, and Germany had only an irregular series of Nazi propaganda programs—in addition to the visual-telephone system.

* *Fern-seh-sprech-stelle*—television speaking place.

In some of its studio programs as late as 1938, Germany was using obsolete mechanical scanning systems, which Britain had discarded early in 1937. The official description of the Berlin television studios, completed in April, 1938, in the Deutschlandhaus on Hitler Square said: "Near the actual stage is the stage manager's room and a waiting room with only a dim blue light, where artists assemble before going on the stage, to accustom themselves to the *semi-darkness in which they must act*." This indicates a type of mechanical, flying-spot-of-light, scanning system of the type discarded by British engineers.

This assumption is corroborated by an article in the January 14, 1938, issue of *World-Radio*, written by its Berlin correspondent:

Two years ago—on January 15, 1936—when the new regular high-definition (sic) television programme service was opened in Berlin, Germany seemed to be far ahead of any other country in television development. But Germany has remained on the standard of 180 lines and twenty-five frames per second, and the Berlin television programme service is restricted to the use of a spotlight scanner for studio work, where artists have to perform in semi-darkness on a sloping stage. The slow-and-sure methods of the Post Office engineers do not permit of a speedy advance into the realm of a real television service for the public.

Very shortly, Germany, with the introduction of the 441-line standard and the opening of three ultra-short wave stations, will again become one of the leading television countries. New studios with full lighting equipment and with iconoscope cameras for use in interiors will at last enable the programme builders to tackle properly the problems of television entertainment. It is hoped that work with 441 lines in these studios will start in April.

It had been hoped that the new 441-line picture service would be ready for the Berlin Radio and Television Exposition in September, 1938, but the engineers had not completed it by then. The new equipment* was not formally placed in service until November 1, and even then there was no regular broadcasting schedule.

When the sporadic public broadcasting "schedule" did begin, it was viewed mostly by groups of people in various public buildings. The receiving sets used were equipped with a large mirror for reflecting the picture from the vertically placed tube. The official in charge of the Post Office televiewing room, at the Ministry of Posts in the Leipzigerstrasse, Berlin, said that a definite service would probably be introduced on January 1, 1939. Unfortunately, the large console receivers would not be available for home use and would cost over two thousand marks, or around $485 at par in 1938. Cheap sight attachments for high-quality radio sets were to be available for around $100.

In the summer of 1939, the German Post Office reported it was preparing to build new television stations in Hamburg, Nuremberg, Munich, and Vienna. On July 26, two days before the opening of the annual German Radio and Television Exposition, the Post Office declared television would be a regular feature of German life in the future. To this end, it claimed 10,000 television standardized receivers had been built. These would be sold for about 650 marks each when the exposition opened. In Berlin, daily afternoon and evening programs

---

* The 441-line picture equipment depended largely on Telefunken-make iconoscopes for studio programs, and Fernseh-made image dissectors for film programs.

would be broadcast, and although only one station existed, others were under construction.

In 1939 radio exposition in Berlin was noticeably smaller than in previous years, and it was announced there would be no show in Berlin in 1940. On the opening day, General Fellgiebel, Four Year Plan Commissar for the Electrical Industry, gave his first instructions to the German radio industry. All companies must be combined into not more than twelve separate groups, and all groups would, in the future, build the same kind of sets.

The Exhibition was formally begun with a speech by Nazi Propaganda Minister Goebbels. On the wall behind him, emblazoned in large gold letters, was this motto: "Broadcasting is the band that unites all Germans in spirit and in mind to this and the other sides of the frontiers."

In his speech, Goebbels declared, "Broadcasting has the duty, wherever it may be required, to start beating down and fighting from the very beginning. To help in this is an honorable and political duty. Broadcasting must stand at its post to fight against (sic) lies and misrepresentations, and is next to the press, the sharpest weapon in the battle of our people. May broadcasting always remain so, and may it continue in the future to broadcast the voice of the Führer, which awakened the nation, and today calls the whole world back to reason!"

Despite repeated announcements of a regular public television service, it had not become a reality in Berlin or anywhere else in Germany when the Nazi forces began their invasion of Poland in September. The promised 10,000 sets had not been built, because raw materials and labor were going into war production, and in August it was promised that regular programs would begin in December—*if* any sets were available. (They were not.)

Nevertheless, the Nazis claimed that, in the *future*, German television would be superb! Commenting on this in a letter sent out of Germany shortly before the war broke out, the Berlin *World-Radio* journalist wrote:

It seems sad that after sixteen good years of development, lively invention, and keen technical activity, German radio progress must halt . . . so as to save foreign exchange and to liberate workers for other and sterner duties. The radio industry is busy with contracts for communication apparatus required by the evergrowing giant army, for Germany will have between one and a half and two million men under arms in August.

In Italy there had been television experimentation for a number of years, based on various mechanical systems. In December, 1938, the Rome-Berlin Axis having been in effect for nearly a year, the Senior Partner's television set a precedent later followed in most every other field. It moved in on Rome. During the Yuletide season which followed the seizure of Austria and the Munich sell-out, the Fernseh company set itself up in Rome.

Italy's first television broadcasting service began the following summer, ostensibly under the auspices of the E.I.A.R.—Ente Italiano per le Audizione Radiofoniche! —the Italian broadcasting corporation. The service was opened at 9:30 P.M. on July 22, 1939 in a hall set aside for that purpose at the "Seaside in Town" summer village in the Circus Maximus. It was announced that programs would be given each (sic) evening—public admitted free of charge.

The transmitter was located on Monte Mario. The service area for its 405-line pictures was reported to extend out about thirty miles from Rome.

In Japan, television experiments with mechanical scanning systems were begun around 1925. *Apparently* little was accomplished during the two decades which followed—at least no reliable information about it was available. The best that can be done is to piece together what little information there is and let you draw your own conclusions.

On December 8, 1936, the newspaper, *Japan Times and Advertiser*, announced a governmental appropriation of nearly 500,000 yen for television research. Zworykin's iconoscope system was to be used, with additional improvements by the engineer in charge—Professor Kenjiro Takayanagi, of the Hamamatsu Higher Technical School.

On August 25, 1937, the United States Department of Commerce reported the establishment of a company in Japan, to be known as Nissan Television Kaisha, formed to operate patents of the Electrical and Musical Industry Company (E.M.I.) of England by the Japan Industry Company, a holding corporation.

On February 25, 1938, the Tokyo press reported the Japan Broadcasting Corporation would start television tests at the end of the month, in preparation for temporary broadcasts in Tokyo the following July. The transmitter was to have a power of only 500 watts, and receivers were to cost around 1000 yen each. The size of

the picture was to be 20 to 22 centimeters square—
roughly seven inches square.

Judging by the occasional official announcements,
every time a new technical improvement was made in
the United States, Professor Takayanagi and his assistants set out to duplicate it.

On May 13, 1939, the first television program for experimental purposes reportedly went on the air from a
newly constructed transmitter in the research laboratory
of the Japan Broadcasting Corporation, at Kamata in
the outskirts of Tokyo. According to the technical reports issued by the Corporation, the equipment and
standards seemed to be just about the same as those in
use by RCA at the highly publicized opening of the
New York World's Fair—the details of which would
already have been known in Tokyo for some time.

In January, 1940, the Japan Broadcasting Corporation
promised it would start a regular program schedule in
the summer of 1940 and would install receivers in Tokyo
department stores and public places.

That is the record, but to assume that any public
broadcasting service began in Tokyo in 1940 would be
to assume a lot.

And that is the record, as far as could be ascertained
through the veil of military censorship, of what happened to television in some fifteen different countries—
up to the time "total war" engulfed each or threatened
it.

Public television broadcasting stopped in every country save two, although its technical development for
military purposes was continued. In Germany, sporadic

television programs continued for a time to advertise the glories of Nazidom.

In the United States, television continued its steady growth—and began to prove its value in a country at war while Japanese bombs were falling on Pearl Harbor.

CHAPTER TWENTY

Television Goes to War

IN the late 1930's, while the Axis was holding its dress rehearsal for war in Spain, Albania, Ethiopia, and China, it was also waging a full-scale war on the fourth front—the propaganda front. During this period the art of propaganda was so highly developed that it became an art to be able to distinguish truth from untruth. This was equally true of politics and information about technical developments, such as television.

In the last chapter, on Axis television, I have tried to present as accurate a record of what happened as possible. The *facts* were few and the record scanty. For that reason it was necessary to limit the chapter to a brief sketch, a suggestion. To have done otherwise would have meant the introduction of personal speculation, when, under the circumstances, a job of accurate reporting was called for.

To have embroidered on the facts myself, to have said, in effect, "Here is the confidential, inside dope, straight from a highly placed Nazi. . . ." would have seemed more sensational—but why do it? It would not be true, and there has been so much of this dubious type of speculation tossed about in recent years. If you give it a moment's thought, you will recognize how perfectly obvious it is that only a few political leaders and generals, in any given country, would know the *complete* story of television in that land.

However, it is possible for the informed observer to recognize something of what is going on by gathering together all the available facts. To attempt to draw conclusions beyond a certain point is about as reliable as playing the stock market by astrology. To have indicated the world-wide spread of television is, in this case, as far as we want to go. Beyond this point we are venturing into a field where there are few reliable facts. The complete story of television's use by the Axis may never be known—certainly not for some years.

As we come now to the story of American television at war, the record is more complete—save for those details of television's military use which must, for obvious reasons, remain pretty much undiscussed.

World War II has the dubious distinction of being the first war in which television has been used. Like sound radio it is employed both in civilian defense and military operations. Unlike sound radio, its uses are little known and of unrecognized importance. But, after all, sound radio—a veteran of many wars—would be more familiar to the public.

Sound radio received its baptism of fire in the South African Boer War of 1899-1902. Then it was still in the archaic form which Sir Oliver Lodge had demonstrated at Oxford in 1894. Its range and value were limited.

Subsequently it was used in the Russo-Japanese War

of 1904-1905, the Turkish-Italian War at Tripoli in 1911, and the Balkan Wars of 1911 and 1912.

In the First World War, sound radio was developed with great rapidity, making it technically ready for the rapid growth of broadcasting in the 1920's. In the same way, the Second World War has brought many new technical advances to television. But, in 1939, television was relatively farther advanced than was sound radio in 1919. Television, in 1942, was roughly in the same stage of *technical* development that sound radio was in 1925. The only thing holding it back was the very considerable obstacle of military-economic necessity. Nevertheless, television had a part to play in the war.

In England, it had started to go to war as early as 1938, when it covered the return of Neville Chamberlain from his "peace in our time" meeting with Hitler. Shortly thereafter, the BBC began to televise demonstrations of antiaircraft defenses, air-raid precautions, and how to put out incendiary bombs. These proved to be some of the best programs they did.

Peter Purbeck, television critic of the BBC magazine, *The Listener*, wrote of these programs: "They have been sent out because instruction on the subject is of vital importance to every member of the public, and television is one of the best ways of disseminating that instruction. If it were not that television in its present stage reaches only a section of the population, there is no doubt that it would prove the ideal method." More than three years later, American television proved this to be true in New York as well. Unfortunately, English television was not to realize its place in the war effort, as we have seen.

To put one's finger on the date when American television began to go to war is difficult. One date might be July 1, 1941—the formal beginning of the era of "commercial" operation. At 2:30 o'clock that afternoon, without any fanfare of any sort, CBS Television went on the air with television's first, up-to-the-minute, visualized news service, stressing the geographical aspect of the world-encircling war and America's position in it.

The exact minute when American television went formally into total war is also difficult to fix. As far as I know, CBS Television Station WCBW, in New York, was the first to be ready with a complete, *visualized* news coverage of the attack on Pearl Harbor. Anticipating such an event months in advance, the CBS Television News Department had prepared graphic maps of all possible war areas—including the Pacific area. These maps, and associated material, had been planned out and to a great extent completed during the preceding summer, when it became obvious that war in the Pacific was a probability.

December 7, 1941, was a Sunday, and WCBW—operating under an experimental license at that time—was not transmitting programs on Sundays. At around 2:40 P.M., Adrian Murphy, Executive Director of CBS Television, issued the order to put the station on the air and cover the outbreak of war in the Pacific. A large proportion of the station's staff was away for the weekend, yet within an hour and a quarter a program was prepared and ready to go on the air. Japanese attacks on Pearl Harbor were still going on, and the news was still fragmentary and often unconfirmed. Therefore, it was decided to wait for further dispatches and then present a complete, rounded picture of the day's happenings. At 8:45 P.M., WCBW went on the air. The program, given by Gilbert Seldes, CBS Television Program Director, and myself, included a round-up of the news, together with latest bulletins and background developments to add perspective. This was visualized with pictures, around two dozen graphic maps, charts, montage effects and other materials.

The outbreak of hostilities emphasized the need for caution and self-censorship in the radio-television industry. Each station was expected to comply with certain obvious rules, but no direct consorship was imposed by the government. Each station was its own direct censor.* It was a tribute to American broadcasting that this procedure could be followed successfully.

In December, 1941, the American Television Society went to work on plans to enlarge the New York television audience of some fifty thousand people into "the largest single defense class in the country." It proposed the formation of groups, which would gather around neighborhood television receivers to receive instruction in air-raid precautions and civilian defense. To this end it tried to get receivers placed in schools, clubs, hotels, and other public places.

---

* One thing banned from the air was weather reports, since submarines off the coast could pick them up and profit by the knowledge. No mention of weather conditions was to be made on the air. This was quite simple for sound radio, but on a television outdoor program there could be no talk of the weather yet the camera would *show* what the weather was like. A television program will sometimes travel 100 to 200 miles out to sea, for there are no mountains or steel buildings to interfere. If television stations made a practice of revealing weather conditions, it would be quite likely that enemy submarines and warships would soon be equipped with television receiving sets. So—television became somewhat allergic to sunshine and showers.

As the year 1942 began, *Radio Daily* noted that despite the Sword of Damocles hanging precariously over television in the form of priorities, there was rapidly accumulating evidence that:

Through their own initiative and endeavor, in conjunction with certain non-industry groups, notably the American Television Society and Government and civilian defense agencies, the television broadcasters are well on the way toward easing the priorities pinch by making their medium indispensable to the war effort.

Already a beginning has been made in this respect. A number of Government agencies, heretofore apathetic or merely tolerantly co-operative with the television stations, are interested in the medium from the long-range point of view of building whole series of elaborately produced programs.

Although the official status of television's priorities had not been decided and the immediate future was of necessity uncertain, television executives were making their medium as useful as possible in the national war effort. Program schedules were devoted largely to this end.

On January 5, 1942, NBC's New York television station, WNBT, telecast an instruction film of the O.C.D. which showed how to extinguish an incendiary bomb. This was followed by a 40-minute lecture and demonstration of air-raid warden tools. The program was viewed by thousands of air-raid wardens at 123 receivers in fifty different precincts of New York City. Reaction was immediate and highly favorable. Television, as the BBC had found in 1938, was particularly suitable for such instruction. It was the only me-

dium that could reach the eyes and ears of thousands of
people in the area bounded, roughly, by Bridgeport,
Connecticut; Trenton, New Jersey; and Poughkeepsie,
New York, and give them the same standardized training all at the same time.

As a result of this test broadcast, New York's Police
Commissioner, Lewis J. Valentine, incorporated television into the official civilian defense organization of
the city, and sets were installed in police stations in every
precinct. Here the air-raid wardens could gather for instruction courses, which began a few weeks later.

In the March, 1942, issue of *Electronics*, Noran E.
Kersta, of NBC, wrote:

The keynote of television today is the role it is playing in
national defense. Television, the ultimate of all communication media, combines the virtues of sound radio and motion
pictures and has additional advantages of its own.

In New York City it is now used as the chief method of
training air-raid wardens. At present the first group of
54,000 prospective wardens are obtaining their training in
the five boroughs of New York City alone where receivers
are installed in all police station classrooms.

. . . it is difficult to train a sufficient number of qualified
instructors to do the job in such a large number of locations.
There is always a best lecturer for any subject. It is this best
lecturer that can authentically instruct all parties instantaneously and uniformly through television. Standardization
of training is thus introduced into the defense plan and considerable economies are effected in the time of the government's instructors.

New York City police officials have expressed the convic-
tion that without television the task of training the tens of
thousands of air raid wardens would be most difficult and
expensive.

In addition to instruction in the five boroughs this same

lecture was transmitted to the entire 60-mile area around New York City where many police centers had been notified to look in. Beyond this 60-mile area, Poughkeepsie, Middletown, and Newburgh received the same instruction via television.

These same courses of instruction were also rebroadcast, simultaneously, by a radio relay network in the area around Troy, Schenectady, and Albany, New York, and in the area around Philadelphia and Camden, New Jersey. In his article, Mr. Kersta noted that with "little investment in effort and material" this network could be extended to Washington, where Du Mont had applied for permission to build a station. Kersta pointed out that through co-operation of sound radio stations air-raid wardens could be quickly assembled to see, on television, "the very latest information that the various intelligence departments of our armed forces are acquiring from day to day concerning enemy activities and methods."

Another facet of television's use in wartime was demonstrated by the CBS station, on January 9, 1942. The audience was invited, in the course of a program, to telephone the station and order Defense Bonds by telephone. The telephones were in the studio, and as each call came in, the caller—and the rest of the audience—could watch his call being received, his questions answered, and the sale of the bond concluded. In less than an hour $75,000 worth of bonds were sold.

A regular feature of WCBW was a complete course of instruction in Red Cross work, put on in conjunction with the Red Cross and directed by Worthington Miner and Ruth Norman.

The range of national defense and war programs was wide—conservation of essential materials, recruiting, civilian defense, news, first aid, discussion forums, propaganda exposés, strategy analysis, celestial navigation and Coast Guard training, documentaries of the various armed forces, geography, geopolitics, basic military training, boxing and dancing entertainment for soldiers and sailors, and a variety of other things.

The public was buying television, too. Despite the fact there was no advertising for the sale of sets, *and* that the public was warned every day of television's uncertain immediate future, *and* that the available receivers were of a 1938 design, *and* it took a long time to get one delivered and installed, *and* it was difficult and often impossible to get any spare parts, the public was purchasing what few sets were available. In New York City they were selling at a rate of about ninety a month, at the beginning of 1942. Ninety a month meant just about the entire available supply in New York.

The wartime status of television still had not been settled by the War Production Board and the Federal Communications Commission. An informal meeting of the F.C.C. and representatives of the television industry was held on April 9, 1942, to discuss the policies to be adopted for television in the war period. As the time for the meeting drew near there was considerable feeling that television would *not* be closed down for the duration.

The points seemed to be in television's favor. For one thing, it represented the quickest, cheapest, and most effective method of mass-training for people in all branches of civilian defense. Television was also the fountainhead of the most modern improvements in radio science—which had become a potent military and political weapon. Beyond that television was generally regarded as the coming big postwar industry—a number one "pilot industry" to take up the slack in employment and industrial productive capacity when the end of hostilities brought an end to mass production of armaments.

Following the hearing on April 9, between the F.C.C. and representatives of the television industry, nothing was heard for some time. On April 17, however, the Defense Communications Board recommended that there be no further construction of radio or television transmitters and stations. This meant it would be impossible to extend the operations of television networks.

On May 12, the F.C.C. announced that the rules governing television stations were changed. Previously a television station had been required to broadcast a minimum of fifteen hours of programs a week to keep its license. This was changed to a minimum of four hours a week, making it possible for stations to conserve vital equipment and operate with much smaller staffs. This also represented a decision to use the entire output of television equipment for the armed services and to put most of the television technicians into building or operating military television equipment. But, by maintaining a minimum requirement of four hours a week, stations could still carry on their most vital programs. In the Commission's words, it would "prevent recession of this new art to a purely experimental or laboratory stage," and it would "keep it alive, ready to flourish as a public service after the war emergency." By the beginning of summer all television stations had condensed

their broadcasting activities to the minimum requirements "for duration," and were concentrating their
efforts almost entirely on programs contributing to the
war effort.

Of the activities of the television companies during
the war, James L. Fly said on June 17, 1942: "Judging
from the accomplishments of the commercial television
industry during the war, you know you have there an
industry which is ready to go and will dominate the
field after the war." *

This was television in action in wartime—on the
home front. But what about television's other wartime
role—as a weapon, in the front lines? Dr. C. B. Joliffe,
engineering executive of RCA and former chief engineer of the F.C.C. had said, on September 11, 1939, he
felt that, if the war lasted more than a few months, it
was probable that television would play an important
part in it. It might become the eye of the army.

At that time a great many scientists in this country
and abroad were already hard at work on the military
uses of television. Scientific research was moving more
rapidly than in the First World War. By 1942, after the
United States had been plunged into the conflict, the
mobilization and use of technical skills was being carried
out on a scale never before approached.

What were some of the military applications of television which were in the course of development? What
is television like—as a weapon of destruction?

* Chairman Fly of the F.C.C. made this statement in the course of his
testimony before the House Interstate and Foreign Commerce Committee
during the hearing on the Sanders Bill.

CHAPTER TWENTY-ONE

Mystery Weapons

THE most obvious use of military television is for observation. There has been much speculation on it, and without doubt every major military power has experimented with it.

Alfred Finestone, writing in *Motion Picture Daily* on September 15, 1939, stated that Arthur A. Lee, Vice-President of Gaumont British "has received information that French planes reconnoitering enemy lines at the western front are experimenting with television sending apparatus. The pictures are received at field headquarters and photographed as they come in."

Similar experiments were carried out in the United States about the same time. For instance, on October 19, 1939, the *New York Times* carried this story:

Television pictures broadcast from Radio City through the National Broadcasting Company's transmitter and aerial atop the Empire State Building were picked up yesterday by a tele-radio set aboard a United airliner 21,000 feet above Washington and 200 miles from New York.

The twenty-one passenger plane left Newark Airport shortly after 9 A.M. and climbing on the line of sight approached the substratosphere to intercept the pictures, since, according to theory, the ultra-short waves that carry the pictures flash off the earth at the horizon on a tangent. Ordinarily, as the engineers explain, television's tiny waves are seen on the earth within a fifty-mile radius. To cover greater distances the receiver antenna must be at a high point through which the beam passes on its straight-line flight.

Technicians regarded the demonstration as a scientific experiment that added proof to the theory that ultra-short waves behave as light waves, following a straight line and, therefore, offer a limited service area on the earth's surface. The effect is best illustrated by a stick laid against a basketball; only a small area of the sphere is touched by the stick.

Televiewers in the metropolitan area looked in on the "show." They saw the announcer at Radio City call the plane. After contact was made, David Sarnoff, president of the Radio Corporation of America, and W. A. Patterson, president of United Airlines, were seen, seated in the National Broadcasting Company's studio at Radio City. . . .

"We are ten miles northeast of Washington at 21,000 feet," said the captain of the plane, "Visibility is clear and unlimited, 10 degrees, temperature." Then an announcer added that the windows were frosted and those in the plane were using oxygen tubes. We are too high to see the ground, but there's a beautiful blue sky, and through it we can see you at Radio City. He described the pictures as generally clear, blemished only occasionally by a few streaks caused by interference from the plane's motors. The announcer found it to be "an eerie sensation" as he watched an NBC photographer in the forward part of the plane taking pictures of Mr. Sarnoff and Mr. Patterson 200 miles away in New York.

The announcer asked the two executives to pose and sit still so the photographer could snap them as they appeared on the screen. When the voice from the sky asked that they smile the effect was as instantaneous as if the photographer were in the studio.

Brig. Gen. Delos C. Emmons, chief of the United States Army General Headquarters Air Force, then came to the plane's microphone to congratulate Mr. Patterson and Mr. Sarnoff on the progress of radio and aviation. He described the experiment as "perfectly wonderful," something to make the imagination run riot, and added that he could distinguish the designs in Mr. Sarnoff's necktie, so clear were the images.

The plane landed in Washington and shortly after noon went aloft again with representatives of the F.C.C., Civil Aeronautics Authority and the Army and the Navy, so that they might look in on New York's new airport at North Beach where the television mobile unit of the NBC was stationed to telecast. The scenes relayed by the truck were intercepted at the Empire State Building for projection into the air above the national capital.

Flying from Washington en route to North Beach, the plane's passengers were entertained by movies telecast from New York. At the landing, in midafternoon, those on board caught a ground-crew view of their arrival as the mobile van televised the scene of the plane returning to earth after a day of chasing elusive images through the skies.

On March 6, 1940, another aerial experiment was carried out by RCA. An account of it appeared in *Motion Picture Daily* the next day:

A striking demonstration of the possible uses of television in wartime was given by NBC yesterday.

Army and Navy observers watching the experiment from private sets were reported as being amazed by the reception. Portable cameras, the lightest thus far constructed, were mounted in an airplane which circled Manhattan Island, and the image they picked up was received at the Empire State building and retransmitted by W2XBS.

Military experts believe that the observation of enemy troop movements by scouting planes equipped with television cameras can be of inestimable value in the event of war. Offshore maneuvers of enemy battleships and offensive tactics on land could be closely watched by the use of such equipment.

Reporters watched the demonstration in the RCA building while aviation editors observed it from a set installed in another United Air Lines plane, which flew alongside the first airplane.

The plane flew at heights varying from 2,000 to 3,000 feet. A slight haze obstructed the view but the camera's sensitivity to infra-red rays (which constitute a considerable nuisance in the studio) pierced the mist.

Editors in the companion plane had the unique thrill of seeing their own plane on the television screen. The signal was received successfully at the General Electric television station near Schenectady.

In the summer of 1940, engineers of the Du Mont Laboratories took their mobile transmitter and went out on field maneuvers with the United States Army. Using a portable camera camouflaged to escape detection, observation posts were set up in the "front lines." Officers at headquarters saw everything that was happening at the "front" as it happened.

On the other side of the ocean, the German Luftwaffe was beginning the aerial blitzkrieg against England. There have been rumors, which of course cannot be confirmed, that German bombers in daylight raids over London were equipped with television cameras, making it possible for officers back at headquarters to see what destruction was being wrought and watch as the bombs exploded in the city.

Television has not only been used for observation in daylight but also, at times, when the human eye cannot see—at night and in heavy fogs. One branch of this is the kind of television which has been descriptively labeled "noctovision." You will remember that John L. Baird was experimenting with it in 1926 and 1927.

In his earlier television experiments Baird had found that the very intense light needed to get a picture caused discomfort to people being televised. It occurred to him that one way to correct this would be to use *invisible light* instead of visible light. As was mentioned earlier in this book, all kinds of light, visible and invisible, are similar to radio waves—all are different manifestations, different kinds of vibrations, of the same thing. Visible light is just one small section of the entire business. The spectrum of visible light includes the colors beginning with red (which has the longest wave length) and running through orange, yellow, green, blue, indigo, to violet (which has the shortest wave length of visible light).

Just beyond each end of this visible spectrum the light becomes invisible. The invisible light, which has a slightly *longer* wavelength than red light, is called *infrared,* meaning "below red." The invisible light, which has a slightly *shorter* wave length than violet light, is called *ultraviolet,* meaning "above violet." (Both of these were first identified in the early part of the nineteenth century.) It was this kind of invisible light which Baird decided to try.

First he tried ultraviolet rays, but they proved objectionable and unsatisfactory. Then he went to the other end of the spectrum and tried infrared rays.

Infrared light has no bad effect on one and has great penetrating power. Although the human eye cannot see it, Baird was able to construct a photo-electric cell which could "see" it. As a result, back in 1926, he could place someone in a dark room and yet see the person, by infrared-ray television, even though the subject could not see his hand before his face. It was this experiment which caused Alexander Russell, writing in *Nature* in 1927, to say, "The direct application of Mr. Baird's invention in warfare . . . seems highly probable. . . ."

This form of television Baird called "noctovision"— night vision. The scope of its application becomes more apparent when you consider that infrared rays penetrate through fog. Mist, fog, and smoke are penetrated by light proportionately to the fourth power of the wave length. In simpler words, the shorter wave lengths of light—such as ultraviolet, violet, blue, and green—are quickly filtered out by haze or fog. Longer wave lengths —such as yellow, orange, and red light—will penetrate through a great deal more fog or smoke than the blues and violets. And infrared light will penetrate fog completely—much better than visible red light.

Perhaps the most common example of this is the sun. Take an average, clear day. At noon, when the sun is directly overhead and shining straight down, it passes through a comparatively thin layer of the earth's atmosphere—with its dust, mist, and inevitable smoke. The sunlight at noon is pure white because all the different wave lengths of pure white light reach the earth. White light, you will remember, is an equal blending of all the different color lights in the spectrum—as Sir Isaac Newton found out, in Chapter Four. However, when the sun begins to set over on the horizon it shines down on an angle and therefore is passing through a much larger amount of the earth's atmosphere, hundreds of miles more. This means it passes through a lot more dust, mist, clouds or fog, and smoke. For this reason the violet, blue, and green light is filtered out—and only the red and infrared light comes through. Result—as you know—the sun looks like a ball of red fire when it sets.

John Baird, following his 1927 experiments, built a "noctovisor" receiver, which was demonstrated publicly in August 1929. It could see in the dark and in the densest fog. When it was perfected, it would be able to locate, through fog and darkness, the movement of ships, of automobiles, and airplanes.

Eight years later, Vladimir Zworykin was reported to have developed in the course of his television experiments an "electron telescope." It pierced darkness, distance, and haze by use of infrared rays. Astronomers were experimenting with it, trying to probe the limitless distances of the universe which lie beyond the range of ordinary telescopes.

Television cameras were built to locate airplanes in the sky, at night and in fogs, by detecting the infrared rays given off by the motors.

In 1938, a patent was awarded for a method of detecting objects which did not emit infrared rays. The idea was simple and ingenious. Assume that a warship, completely blacked out and emitting no infrared rays, is hidden in a dense fog on a moonless night. Assume that its engines have been stopped, making it impossible to detect it by hydrophones, sonic detectors which pick up the sound of engines and propellers. Working together are a television camera, sensitive to infrared rays, and a powerful "searchlight" which gives off a beam of infrared rays. The "searchlight" probes through the fog with its penetrating beam, and the camera follows its movement. When the beam passes across the steel warship, the infrared rays will be reflected back and picked up by the camera. Thus the location of the warship is determined.

Using this method, with two such units installed in the searching vessel, it would be possible to determine not only the general area in which the enemy warship was hidden but also its exact direction and distance. This is possible by using the stereoscopic effect obtained by seeing with two eyes instead of one. It has been in military use for years in artillery range-finders, ashore and afloat. These range-finders were useful only when there was no fog and enough light for the human eye to see. With the introduction of a highly developed form of noctovision, the blackest nights and the thickest fogs can be penetrated.

Noctovision can fly as well as swim. A pilot flying a bomber over a blacked-out enemy city would be able to see his target if his plane were equipped with infrared television. Against such equipment the ordinary methods of blacking out are ineffective, even on moonless nights in heavy fog.

Until it was learned that the bombing planes were equipped with noctovision, a blacked-out city might receive as bad (or even worse) a pounding as Rotterdam, London, and Coventry took in 1940. The element of surprise, caused by the introduction of a "mystery" weapon, might be considerable. However, once the secret was learned, a defense could undoubtedly be set up. One such defense would be a "white out" instead of a "black out." It was reported in 1941 that the Russians had used this method with considerable success in the defense of Moscow. When the Nazi bombers came over they found that although the ordinary house and street lights were extinguished, hundreds and hundreds of powerful searchlights blazed up into the sky. The brilliance was so dazzling that military objectives could not be found. This was a "white out" using visible light. The same method could be used against planes equipped with noctovision. Regular, visible searchlights could be used for they also give off infrared rays—heat rays. Or, if it was decided to "black out" a city, then invisible searchlights of infrared rays could be used to "jam" the noctovision cameras. In addition, dummy targets—faked airdromes, factories, and oil tanks—could be "illuminated" with infrared rays (any heating apparatus might do) and used to lure the attacking bombers away from real targets.

In 1941 a patent was granted for an airplane detector. It was suggested the device might detect planes, by infrared rays from its engine. It might also pick up such rays from the smokestacks of a ship. It was designed to detect "the existence of an invisible body radiating heat" and to produce "a visible image of the original heat-radiating body." It might be used to detect the presence of planes hidden in clouds or fog and also used for guiding aircraft to a landing in fog "by visible indications from desired points which are produced by devices radiating heat." In this way, the position of a landing field could be seen on a television receiver in the airplane.

In the early part of 1941, the Sperry Corporation was reported, by *Financial World*, to be interested in a new television instrument called a "radio-contour-meter," which would show the pilot of an airplane the exact altitude at which he was flying and the contour of the earth just ahead of him.

About the same time, a patent was granted to Alfred

N. Goldsmith for an airplane television device. The pilot of a plane could see his airdrome on the screen and the closer he came the larger the picture became.

Another way to use television in aerial warfare was reported to have been discovered by the British at least as early as 1938. It was found that the ultra high frequency waves of television broadcasts could be used to detect airplanes approaching the shores of England, although they were many miles away. The signals from the BBC television transmitter would strike the approaching plane and be reflected back to ground. This discovery was put to work and developed into a sensationally effective airplane detector—which apparently became a keystone in the defense of the British Isles. Such equipment might be installed in night fighter planes—as well as on the ground.

Another and even more sensational aspect of television's use as a weapon is the television aerial torpedo.

In November, 1938, the magazine *Radio and Television* carried an article by U. A. Sanabria. In it he wrote:

In recent months there has been increasing attention given to television as a primary military force. All nations are vitally interested, and with excellent reason; the scope and versatility of this newest science is as astounding to the lay mind as it is unlimited to the General's.

You have probably heard of "Suicide Squadrons." They are the very latest tactical bodies in use by militaristic nations. Under the present application, they are in use in land warfare, aerial warfare, and naval warfare. Deriving their nickname from their mode of operation, they presage certain death to the members of the operating staff. Under normal action a suicide squadron is composed of men who man explosive projectiles. The units they man are literally human bombs, filled with explosives and guided by human hands. It naturally follows that such projectiles are the most deadly which have been yet devised. In the form of land vehicles, aerial craft, and water sleds, they are characterized by their high speed and extreme maneuverability. Useful as weapons of defense and offense, they concentrate upon destruction of the enemy at the cost of the life of the human operator. Such squadrons are comparatively rare, though, and the tacticians refrain from their use except as a last resort. In spite of the glory which attends the "suicide," men do not care to throw away their lives carelessly.

Imagine, now, a small, perfectly streamlined and radio-controlled airplane. Its guiding transmitter is located in a larger plane. In addition to its radio receiver, this remote-controlled diminutive airplane carries a load of explosives in its fuselage, capped by the ordinary mechanism which sets off the blast upon contact with its target. This radio-controlled torpedo has been successfully demonstrated and can be used at present if desired.

In August, 1940, it was reported that Lee de Forest was working with Sanabria in the perfection of such a television plane. *Radio Daily* wrote a short time later:

Dr. Lee de Forest expects the development of a pilotless "television torpedo plane" on which he and U. A. Sanabria, president of American Television Laboratories, Chicago, have been experimenting, to be completed within a year. Device, which is now being tested at Wright Field, near Dayton, Ohio, can be made of comparatively cheap plastics or similar material and would require no armor or other expensive devices.

The torpedo would carry no human beings, as its flight would be directed by radio from a mother ship ten or more miles away. Iconoscopes would be installed in the torpedo plane's nose and topsides, according to the description of its inventors.

Take this television torpedo plane and equip it with noctovision. Muffle the engine exhaust so it can fly quietly towards its objective at a great height in the middle of the night. Cut off the engine and let it glide down the last thirty miles of its trip in absolute silence —through clouds and fog, invisible and almost inaudible, but under complete control of a navigator who is miles away yet able to see his target. Think of what one such aerial torpedo, carrying several tons of high explosives, could do. But suppose that instead of just one plane there were ten or twenty thousand such planes —and they all were launched in a simultaneous attack on different parts of a country on the same moonless, foggy night.

CHAPTER TWENTY-TWO

The Coming Revolution

WHEN you run down the street in a hurry, you keep your eyes open to see where you are going. It is also a good idea to keep your eyes open as you go hurrying through life. We are all driving steadily into the future at a rate of sixty minutes an hour. It's a good idea to look where we are going and make our plans for the future now. In 1918 we fought a war to end wars. But, after it was over we went on an irresponsible joy ride. We did not look where we were going, and—well—look what happened.

When any person or any nation forgets its responsibilities of the present and does not plan wisely for the future, the result is always the same—disaster.

I do not think you will deny that the fundamental reasons for wars, depressions, and the rise and decline of nations are not individual people or individual races. Rather they are long-range economic trends, which have their roots largely in technological advance. The classic example is the invention of gunpowder by the Chinese centuries and centuries ago. Ever since then the country which had the best guns was able to impose its will on its neighbors.

Or take the American Civil War. General Ulysses S. Grant was the number one general for the North. When his armies defeated those of the South, Grant was a great hero. He was an idol of the North—and toured Europe in honor. The United States elected him President. But Grant did not *win* the war. It was the great production capacity of the Northern states which overwhelmed the nonindustrialized South. And what started the Civil War in the first place? Certainly not a few cannonballs on Fort Sumter. What was much more the cause was the fundamental conflict between the economic systems of the North and the South. The economy of the South had its roots in the invention of the cotton gin by Eli Whitney—half a century earlier. The economy of the North had its roots in such inventions as the steam engine, which led to railroads, steamships, and the use of large mechanized factories.

Today, people should be more conscious of the economic forces underlying the disruptions of modern civilization. In World War II the importance of mass production certainly has been heavily stressed. Wars are not won by individual generals. They are won by the side with the strongest industrial system and which makes the most efficient use of it. Production is *guided* by men who have, or have not, foresight and intelligence. It is *based* upon technological advance—on inventions.

The civilization of the Middle Ages was revolutionized by the development of such inventions as printing and better sailing vessels, both methods of communication, and by the improvement of gunpowder and firearms, which is, after all, a form of communication used when gentler forms of persuasion are ineffective.

Nineteenth-century civilization, a product of that "industrial revolution" we have heard so much about, was largely created as a result of the invention of such forms of communication as the steam locomotive, the steamboat, and the electric telegraph. These "built" the cities of the last century.

Twentieth-century civilization is being completely transformed by other methods of communication—the automobile, the airplane, the telephone—and most recently the movies and the radio.

Look around you in your home. Note how completely the modern forms of communication govern your life, make it entirely different from what it would have been a quarter of a century ago. Take the electric inventions only. The electric light, for instance, has changed the living habits of the world. People no longer live by the sun's hours—going to bed around 8 or 9 P.M. and arising at 5 or 6 A.M. Now people (including myself) go to bed and get up at the craziest times!

Or consider the change in living habits caused by the mechanical refrigerator, the electric washing machine, the electric fan, the air-conditioning machine, the electric razor, the X-ray machine, the sun-ray machine, the dentist's drill, the electric elevator.

The radio has made profound changes in your life, changes too obvious to need listing. It has made changes not only in the life of the individual but in whole nations. It enabled the Nazis to secure their control of the German nation and in a few years completely transform its way of thinking and what it believed.

Sum it up with this: Our entire way of life has been changed, and is now being changed, by the invention of new forms of communication. These inventions are the great revolutionists of the world—not Karl Marx and Lenin. On the contrary, these men recognized the implications of modern inventions long before the rest of the world did. Their actions were motivated by the underlying economic forces, stemming, in the final analysis, from technological advances.

The trends of the future can be clearly seen in the inventions of yesterday and today. Yesterday, as the result of a compound-invention by many men, television broadcasting became possible. Today you buy a television set—a straightforward purchase of a machine. Tomorrow it has begun to change your life.

Inventions are made. Some of them are adopted, put into use. Then the powder train is lit. Countless new uses are found for it and countless social effects and changes result from it—inevitably. The invention of the radio and its subsequent use has exerted more influence on twentieth-century civilization than the conception and subsequent life of Adolf Hitler.

Inventions, however, do not suddenly appear and exert their powers in a day. In almost every instance there has been a considerable period of time elapsing between the moment of invention and the moment of practical use. This is particularly true of inventions which subsequently changed civilization the most.

The introduction of the movable type printing press by Gutenberg, in 1439 and 1440, did not completely transform civilization before January 1, 1441, or even 1541. It took centuries for printing to reach maturity and to give rise to newspapers, magazines, and mass production of books. The transforming effect of printing was spread over hundreds of years.

The introduction, in modern times, of the movies and the sound radio caused a much more rapid transformation of society. To be sure, radio and movies were introduced in a civilization already highly developed and capable of reacting more quickly. Nevertheless, the movies and the radio were presented to the public in an infant state. Movies were flickering peepshows, and radio was a set of squeaky headphones. As they developed from this crude state to their present degree of perfection they exercised a gradually increasing effect on the world. Movies have been exerting a noticeable effect over a period of roughly three decades, at minimum. Radio, at minimum, over two decades.

Television, on the other hand, was kept in the laboratory until it was nearly full-grown. As an art, it was born an adolescent, almost ready to exert a grown-up effect on society.

What is television? Is it an amalgam of movies, radio, and theater? The answer is—No. It borrows something from each of these three fields, but the result is more than the sum of the parts. Television is potentially a new art, with powers and characteristics peculiar to itself. It combines the aural powers of radio with the visual attraction of movies, newspapers, and magazines. To this it adds an appallingly powerful sense of actuality—a feeling that one is actually present at the event which is taking place, that one is in two places at one time. The impact of television is potentially greater than the combined impacts of sound radio, and movies, and theater, and newspapers—all put together. This is the power of television—and, as experience will prove, it is not over-statement.

Unquestionably such a medium is the most powerful which has ever been devised. It is staggering to contemplate.

Television is not bursting upon the world in a flash. As we have seen, it has been developing a long time. But, the period of application *is* at hand. It has already been in practical use for some time, getting steady on its feet. It is just beginning to exert its influence on society. It does not even guess its full strength. Modern Aladdins have uncorked a modern genie. Let us hope we can control it.

Now is the time to recognize the power of television. Instead of running ahead with closed eyes, it is wiser to look ahead, to understand the implications of the cliché —"Television is here." It is not to be disposed of in a chapter. It is a problem demanding careful thought by many people in many books. It is *not* a problem that can be solved by nineteenth-century free and *unrestricted* enterprise. It demands cautious, careful planning and conscientious self-discipline.

Fortunately for the people of the United States, this has been the policy of the Federal Communications Commission—hostile journalists to the contrary. I think the record, which I have tried to set down impartially and accurately in this book, proves it.

As to the government's policy during the war period and thereafter, here it is, as expressed in a letter I received in 1942 from James L. Fly, Chairman of the Federal Communications Commission. He wrote:

This is . . . a statement of the Commission's view of television during the present war period, and in the decade following the war.

In 1941 the Commission found, after the fullest consideration of all factors, that television was then technically ready to move ahead on a full commercial basis. This did not, of course, mean that further technical improvement would cease; but it did mean that development was already such as to justify full use of the new medium; and it further meant that promulgation of standards at that time would not limit or hinder further development. This decision was reached with the full approval of television engineers both in and out of the industry and the Commission.

The war and victory programs, however, with their vast demands for men, machines, and material, have made any large-scale expansion of television during the war impossible. No doubt technical progress will continue, partly in connection with military uses of television and partly as a by-product of other wartime research.

The result, if we are to embark on prophecy, will no doubt be that demobilization day will find television a fully explored but wholly unexploited field. We can anticipate a widespread demand for consumer goods such as television sets, many factories able and ready to convert back from war production to such consumer goods, and all the other factors necessary for the most rapid post-war television expansion.

I think it quite likely that during the post-war period television will be one of the first industries arising to serve as a cushion against unemployment and depression. Radio broadcasting served that function in a measure during the 1920's; by 1926 it had achieved a half-billion dollar gross turnover, though at the close of the war, wireless was far less developed than television will be at the close of this war. There is no reason now apparent why we should not aim at a 50,000,000-set television industry mirroring the present 50,000,000-set standard broadcast industry.

Sincerely yours,
James Lawrence Fly

Even if you never expect to go inside a television studio, even if you are blind and deaf, you cannot ignore television because it will affect your life. The myth of isolationism has been pretty well debunked by recent events.

Remember that once an invention is put into use, the powder train is lit. Perhaps at first only one single use may be made of a given invention. But this results in certain social effects, which in turn cause new uses to be made of the invention and also additional social effects. It spreads like wildfire in all directions. When Edison had perfected the phonograph, he thought it a good idea to have some visual gadget to accompany it. So he filmed the first moving picture. Look what happened.

Let me list just a few of the *most* obvious, direct uses of television. Think them over and recognize the social changes which can result from each. I will not try to do more than just suggest these matters here. To go into each use with any thoroughness would require a separate book in each case. And as you glance over this list, keep in mind the fact that television is potentially more powerful than radio, movies, and newspapers put together. And despite many obstacles and forms of opposition, television has already grown to a considerable size. It will keep on growing, more rapidly all the time. Certain things have, in the past, slowed it down, but it cannot be stopped. For anyone, or any industry, to try to stop it or ignore it would be futile. It would only work to the disadvantage of the obstructionist. Look what happened to the phonograph industry, in the 1920's, when it tried to ignore the growth of sound radio broadcasting.

Television means, first of all, a new medium of entertainment and instruction. New types of programs, new art forms which have never been seen before. New methods of education. Unlike many other technological advances, television will not necessarily throw people out of work. On the contrary, it will create thousands of new jobs—for technicians, for actors and dancers, for writers, and for dozens of other kinds of workers. To be sure, television will have an effect on motion pictures and sound radio and newspapers and magazines. Horrid lurking fears torment some executives in these industries —but to a large extent this need not be.

Television need not be a bogeyman to newspapers, motion pictures, sound radio, or magazines. It will force these fields to overhaul their production methods and improve the quality of their products, but the far-seeing and intelligent editor or producer can derive new benefits from television, find new markets, by recognizing its inevitability and co-operating with it instead of fighting it.

Television means not only a new entertainment medium, but also a new form of education, whether it is in the field of fine arts, surgery, or extinguishing fire bombs. Television can make a classroom of an entire nation. When the President makes a fireside chat, people will see the President sitting beside them in their own homes. A great surgeon can perform a delicate operation, and a hundred thousand medical students, in hundreds of cities, can watch and learn.

Television means a new form of journalism. Up-to-the-minute coverage of the news of the world, in visual and aural form.

In other words, a television set in your home is a combination movie theater, museum, educator, news reporter, playhouse, daily picture magazine, political forum and discussion center, propaganda and counter-propaganda dispenser, art gallery, vaudeville show, opera and ballet theater, plus a few other things rolled into one.

Television is also a new branch of the business world—a new form of advertising, infinitely more powerful than any other form. The salesman can now step into the customer's home and actually show his merchandise —not just in black and white but in its natural color. Advertising in newspapers and magazines is much more expensive if it is done in color, but television is no more expensive in color than in black and white. Actually, the production costs of advertising by color television may be less than in black and white—and the sales appeal will be infinitely greater. Long-winded sales arguments, so familiar in blind sound-radio, become unnecessary in television. The objectionable part of advertising in radio can be dispensed with by the intelligent television director.

To build the television stations which broadcast the programs, to build the sets which receive them means a new manufacturing industry. Skilled technicians by the thousands, who have been producing military radio and television equipment, as well as tanks, airplanes, guns, and ships, will be needed. Let me stress again what James Fly has said: ". . . demobilization day will find television a fully explored but wholly unexploited field." And at a press conference on March 23, 1942, he indicated his desire to do everything possible to keep television alive and progressing during the war years. "Television," he said, "will be the big postwar industry, and we must keep it going."

The discovery and use of, let us say, radium had a profound effect in medical methods. Properly used it was a boon to mankind. Improperly used it killed. In this respect, television is like radium but with one difference—radium is rare; television is exactly the opposite, for it is destined to encompass the world. With the passing of every day this genie is growing bigger and stronger.

It is clear that the future development of television must be carefully planned and controlled. Any planning involves a risk. Any competent businessman knows that when he buys a stock of raw materials for his future production schedule there is an element of risk involved. He calls it a "good business risk." He knows also that to make no advance plans whatsoever means certain disaster.

A lack of proper planning produced the dust-bowls of the midwestern states. It produced the Wall Street crash of 1929, the depression, and World War II. These are all-too-painful examples of lack of planning.

How is the future development of television to be planned? Will it become the private property of a single corporation, a trust—the Fascist way? Will it become the monopoly of a totalitarian government? Will it have no control at all and run hog-wild to certain chaos? Or is it not possible that the men who planned the Constitution of the United States did such a good job of planning that television can grow in the democratic tradition? By this I mean as private, competitive enterprise, operating in accordance with its own, self-imposed rules and genuinely in the public interest.

So far it has grown in this democratic tradition. There is no reason why it cannot continue that way—if, as seems to be the case, responsibilities are realized and assumed. This means planning for the future as we have done in the past. Such planning demands wisdom and knowledge, a unity of purpose, and courage to act. Such planning is possible in a democracy. It is also vital. Without it a democracy cannot hope to exist.

CHAPTER TWENTY-THREE

P. S.

WE have covered all but about the last half-century of our 4,000 years of television mentioned on the title page and cover. When the first cornerstone was placed on the date peg of 2000 B.C., it suggested our story would end on the date peg of 2000 A.D. Since that is still a few decades away, it would be a bit difficult, not to say presumptuous, to give you an accurate, documented report of television's progress in the last part of the twentieth century.

Did I hear someone give a sigh and mutter, "Here come the prophecies of the future." Sorry, no prophecies today.

I think the pattern is fairly clear, now that we have climbed the family tree of television and are biographically consummate—save for a few second and third cousins, once removed, for whom there was not room. If it is prophecy you want, then look at the pattern, look at the world around you and the history behind you . . . and see if you cannot figure it out for yourself.

P. P. S.—How To Get a Job in Television

HOW to get a job in television—that is a question which a great many people are asking. It would be difficult to estimate the number of times I have heard acquaintances say, "Yes, indeed, television is the coming thing. You are very lucky to be in on the ground floor. But how can I get a job in television?"

There is no magic formula which is sure-fire—except perhaps to marry the Boss's daughter, and there just are not enough daughters to go around. There are, however, some practical, sound suggestions which can be of definite assistance.

During the war years, jobs in television are extremely limited. With the end of hostilities, new jobs will open up in every branch of television, and the demand for new people will increase over a long period of years. The supply of unskilled workers will be large. The supply of partly trained technicians will be moderate. The supply of highly trained workers and artists will be very small.

What kind of jobs will there be? Practically every kind—scientific, mechanical, artistic, business. They will be open to all kinds of people, young and old. But it is well to remember that television is going to move fast. It demands adaptability, quick thinking, and imagination. Much of the work will be done under heavy pressure in the actual broadcasting end of the industry, and techniques and methods will be changing constantly. The men and women who retain their *mental* youth and plasticity and who can work under heavy pressure without losing perspective or health will be the ones who go farthest.

Now let us get down to cases.

Exactly why do you want a job in television? Before we go any further, straighten this out in your own mind. Television has about it a quality of glamour, of mystery, of tinsel optimism. Is that what attracts you? Undoubtedly it does—partly if not completely. For your own sake go a little deeper into the subject.

Do you have a specific objective in mind in going into television—or is it *entirely* the idea that it would be thrilling and fascinating work? If that is all, then stop now and save yourself a lot of unhappiness later on. The dilettante has his place in any art—on the edge in a strictly amateur standing, not in the center of the profession.

What do you want to do in television? Do you want to get into it in one way or another because it is a "coming thing," offering the lure of power and money? In other words—are you strictly an opportunist? If you are, remember that there will not be "big money" in the *immediate* future. Remember also that television is being carefully controlled by the government to prevent rash expansion, unwise promotion, and "get-rich-quick" schemes that might exploit the public. The immense power of television is recognized by our government, and steps have been taken to insure that it does not become concentrated in the hands of any clique or group of irresponsible persons. The air through which television travels is *public property*. Unscrupulous exploitation of this natural resource will not be allowed—the mistakes of the nineteenth century are recognized.

Do you want to get into television work because you genuinely feel it is the place for you, that you can contribute something of value? Do you think you are suited for it? Do you know what sort of job you want?

Think these questions over before going any further.

In seeking a job in television you are, in effect, offering your talents and your efforts for sale. In return you expect to be paid money—which you can exchange for food, clothing, housing, entertainment. You also will be paid other less tangible things—the pleasure of interesting work, the satisfaction of contributing to a worthy cause, knowledge and experience which will qualify you for better jobs and higher salary.

How are you going to go about offering your talents and your efforts? In essence—you have to be a salesman. You are selling a commodity—your services—just as though you were selling an automobile or a bottle of tomato catsup. To do this you must know your product and its uses.

You may know you have certain abilities, even if you never stopped to figure them out, but surely you cannot expect a stranger to know it. Surely you cannot expect to go see an executive of a company and say to him, "I would like a job . . . some kind of a job . . . because . . . well, I want it." If you look for a job that way you are just wasting your time, and the executive's time, and spoiling an opportunity.

You have got to know your product thoroughly. What it has to recommend it . . . what it can do . . . what it has done . . . and why anyone would want it.

If you have never done it before, here is a good way to get acquainted with yourself. Get a pencil and paper. Go off by yourself. Possibly sit down in front of a mirror and take a good long look. Write down on paper, in two lists, what your good points are, and what your bad points are.

What are your personal characteristics—and be frank, because you will be fooling nobody but yourself.

What did you study in school? What do you like and dislike? Did you ever take any psychological tests of aptitudes? What were the results? If you never took any such tests, you might find it valuable and learn a lot about yourself. Perhaps, if your career is important enough to you, you might take the trouble to get in touch with your neighborhood public school or the psychology department of a neighboring college. Ask if you cannot take such a test. All modern schools have them or can tell you where to get them. Explain why you want it.

How do you spend your spare time, and what are you interested in? What sort of things have you done since childhood? Have you studied music? Have you made model airplanes? Think about the last movie you saw— can you analyze why you liked it or disliked it? What was wrong with it? What were its good points?

Ask yourself all sorts of questions—and put down,

on paper, your analysis. Try to get to know yourself. It is one of the most important and most difficult things a person can do. Don't rush. Take all the time you need —a week or a month, if necessary. Surely your career is worth it.

When you have it all down in writing, ask yourself this question: What kind of a job am I fitted for now? What can I do a good job at—now? In what direction do I want to develop? What is my objective—now, and in a year from now, and in ten years from now, and in twenty years from now?

Then when you have gotten that straight in your mind as far as possible, try putting yourself in the position of the executive who hires people. If *you* were the executive, and somebody—with your qualifications— wanted a job, what would you want to know about that person? What would make you want to hire him or her? Figure that out carefully, and put it on paper.

The executive who engages people for various jobs has a responsibility, and if he engages the wrong person, he is blamed for it. He is going to be very certain that you are the right person for the job before he hires you. Therefore, if you will put yourself in his position, if you will look at yourself from his point of view, it will help you to figure out just what you are qualified for or can reasonably expect to do. It will make it easier for you to present your good points in the best light. In addition to that, when a person knows himself and recognizes his good and bad points, he will be more sure of his ground—less uncertain in his approach and more poised without being aggressive or pompous.

A searching self-examination will always reveal a lack of sufficient information and experience in some things. How are you going to get the necessary experience and background information to qualify you for television work? And how are you going to break into the field? Let us take these two questions separately.

First, how are you going to prepare yourself for television work? What experience and knowledge will be helpful?

Roughly speaking, you should have at least a high school education, or the equivalent of it. A college education is still better. What is *most* important is not that you have a diploma from such and such a school, but that you have learned something and have developed your mind and curiosity. It is all too easy to get a college diploma and still be thoroughly uneducated. There are hundreds of thousands of examples walking around the country.

If you are going into the program or business end of television, it is highly desirable to have a rounded cultural background, a "liberal arts" education. First get a broad foundation and then specialize later. The man or woman who is well-read, who has taken the trouble to observe the world around him, who has a lively curiosity, will go farthest. Ask yourself this question: Have I taken the trouble, have I had the curiosity, to learn something about the following fields which will contribute directly to television—literature, physics, music, ballet, theater, motion pictures, sociology, psychology, journalism, history, economics, propaganda analysis, foreign languages, art, typewriting, singing and public speaking, civics and government, sports?

If you want to go into the technical end of television, you will need a highly specialized scientific training—obviously. You can start it in many vocational schools, trade schools, and colleges. A list of colleges giving courses in radio and television will be found in the annual yearbook of such a magazine as *Broadcasting*. Your local Board of Education will be able to give you suggestions and advice. Large electrical manufacturing concerns sometimes maintain schools or offer apprenticeships. Building your own amateur equipment is an excellent way to learn the fundamentals, but if you want to build your own transmitter you should learn the government requirements necessary for a license. Inquire at your local library, or ask the chief engineer of your local radio station. You will also find it very helpful not to make your education too one-sided. Learn something of the artistic and business end of television. Knowledge of music, theater, motion pictures, literature, and economics will pay you in the long run.

Whether you are going into the technical end or the artistic or the business, you will find that you can get only part of the necessary experience and background by going to school. The other part you can get only by having the curiosity to observe what goes on in the world around you, and note its relation, no matter how small, to television—now or in the future. Perhaps the best way to help yourself in this respect is by your own reading.

You do not do this just by attending classes and doing the minimum required work. That will qualify you only to be one of those highly uneducated people who own a diploma. The person who has the imagination and curiosity to learn things by himself is the one who gets ahead.

I have already listed various general fields of knowledge with which you would do well to familiarize yourself. It is entirely up to you. You have access to unlimited material. There is a school or library in every town in the United States. The books are there if you want them. Any librarian, any teacher will be only too happy to make them available to you. There are almost as many bookstores throughout the country, and books are not expensive. When you consider the concentrated and uncensored knowledge in one book, and the work which has gone into it, you will realize how much you can get for practically nothing—what you might spend in a week on cigarettes and chewing gum.

Books on the general fields which I have already listed are easy to find. Not so easy to find is *good* reading material on such a new and specialized field as television. This being true, I have made a list of books, magazines, and newspapers, which you will find of decided value, if you want to learn more about any particular aspect of television. A classification of each is included and you will find the list at the end of this chapter. It will save you a lot of unnecessary searching in a field that is comparatively unorganized and undocumented.

How are you going to get into television? How are you going to go about getting your first job in television, or a job which will lead to television?

First of all, let me stress that there are practically no

jobs available in television *broadcasting* during the war period, particularly for men. After the war there will be jobs, in increasing numbers—and you can prepare yourself in the interim. If you are interested in the *technical* end, there is a shortage now. Technicians are needed in war industries and in the armed forces. Thousands are being trained for work in war industries and thousands more are being trained in the Army and Navy. Unlimited opportunities to acquire the technical training necessary for television exist in war industries and the armed forces. Thousands upon thousands of these engineers will find good jobs available in television after demobilization—after the war is won.

What sort of jobs will be available in the artistic and business ends of television? Roughly the same as those in radio and motion pictures. Below they are listed briefly in groups according to type:

Actors, announcers, MC's (masters of ceremonies), commentators, dancers, singers, and musicians.

Writers and editors.

Directors, assistants, producers, script girls, production assistants.

Secretaries, stenographers, receptionists, page boys.

Painters, designers, production managers, stage managers, stagehands.

Cameramen, dolly-pushers, microphone boom operators.

Salesmen, publicity men, businessmen, research men, psychologists.

Engineers, technicians, physicists, chemists, constructors.

What can you do to prepare yourself for one of these jobs? There are three ways:

(1) Formal education in schools and colleges which give courses in radio and television, and in subjects allied to television.

(2) By your own initiative in educating yourself by reading and observing. Watch television broadcasts and analyze them. Note what is wrong with them—and there is always plenty to note. Figure out the reasons for what is wrong—technical, artistic, economic, political, social, military. Watch movies and analyze them. The same applies to plays, ballets, opera, and radio. Note their relation to television. Analyze the appeal and methods of newspapers—their news handling, their political bias, their features. Do the same with magazines, particularly such magazines as *Life*, *Look*, and *Coronet*. Note the techniques of the newspaper *PM*. Analyze the appeal and methods of the fashion magazines, such as *Vogue*, *Harper's Bazaar*, *Mademoiselle* and *Glamour*. Look at Bonwit Teller's windows. Understand the role of propaganda in radio—an admirable account is contained in the book *Radio Goes to War* by Charles J. Rolo, Putnam's, 1942.

(3) Learn as much as you can about the workings of radio, motion pictures, and all forms of theater. Learn something of photography. If you have your own camera, so much the better. Learn the fundamentals of pictorial composition.

Any form of work in the professional theater is very difficult to find, but dramatic experience is of inestimable value. If you cannot get it professionally, you certainly can get it on an amateur basis—and that is often preferable. Get it in school and college dramatics. Learn all aspects of it. Writing, acting, make-up, directing, lighting, costuming, dancing, fencing, singing. A course in a good drama school is excellent—although good drama schools are rare. Perhaps you can find some local dramatic group which can give you some experience.

Go after radio experience. That is just as valuable. Organize a dramatic group and, when you have a short sketch well-rehearsed, ask for an audition at a small, local radio station. If you are any good, the station will probably be interested. You will not be paid, but if you can get some time on the air it will give you good experience.

Then, go after a staff position on a *small* radio station —as a continuity writer or a salesman or an announcer or a receptionist or a page. Anything to get a foothold. Once you have it, you will find you can work into other fields. The *best* way to start in radio is in a small station. Here you can get an opportunity to do all kinds of work. If you keep your eyes open, if you are intelligent and enterprising, if you keep reading, studying, observing, you can get more valuable experience in a year or two in a small station than you can in twice that time at a large station. In the small station you can see everything that goes on. You can examine the essence of radio. You can acquire a perspective which you cannot get in a large station, where the organization is so big, so complex, that you are limited in your observation, departmentalized in your work.

You can also start as a page boy or an apprentice in a large radio station, but you will never quite get the same experience you get in a small station. Small station work means as much in radio as a background in stock and vaudeville used to mean in theater.

These, then, are the three general approaches, which, for best results, should all be used.

But how to approach the station manager for your first staff job?

You have already—if you are smart—analyzed yourself and looked at yourself from the executive's viewpoint. With your written notes, and with an understanding of what your selling points are, sit down and go to work on a letter.

Do *not* walk into a station and ask to see the manager. Do *not* call up on the phone and ask for a job. Sit down and write a straightforward business letter. Set down first why you are writing, what *specific* kind of a job you want, and why you want it. Then, in the next paragraph, briefly note the reasons why you are qualified for such a job, and what you can contribute.

Be brief—never more than one page. Typewrite if you can, or at least write legibly. Remember that your letter is your advance salesman. You will be judged by it. If it is not well-composed, if it seems indecisive or overly aggressive, if it looks messy, you probably will *not* be invited in for an interview. Take plenty of time, and work out the letter until it is as good as you can make it. All this may seem complicated, but it works.

For those interested—here are some sources of further information about television:

The suggested books will supply a general background of information. For up-to-the-minute developments, see the various suggested magazines. It would be well to check over the back issues of the magazines. Most, if not all, can be found in the large libraries in big cities. Many of the books will be found in smaller libraries. In every case the publisher's address is given, so you can write for a copy of the book or magazine in question if you cannot find it in your library:

The Annals (of the American Academy of Political and Social Sciences, Philadelphia.) Issue of January, 1941, *New Horizons in Radio* (Vol. 213). Survey of radio, television, and facsimile.

Color Television: Goldmark-CBS process. Complete description in April, 1942, issues of *Journal of the Society of Motion Picture Engineers* and *Proceedings of the I.R.E.* See also *Electronics,* October, 1940, and *Direction,* October 1940, page 14.

Communications, a monthly, published by the Bryan Davis Publishing Company, 19 East 47th Street, New York. Technical developments. See back issues.

Electronics, published monthly by McGraw-Hill, 330 West 42nd Street, New York. Technical developments. See back issues.

Engines of Democracy, by Roger Burlingame. Scribner's, New York, 1940. Effect of inventions on society.

Facsimile and Its Future Uses, by J. V. L. Hogan. See *Annals.*

Frequency Modulation by Edwin Armstrong. See *Annals.*

Journal of the Society of Motion Picture Engineers, monthly. Business address: Hotel Pennsylvania, New York. Technical developments in movies and television. See back issues.

QST, published monthly by American Radio Relay

League, West Hartford, Conn. For amateurs. See back issues.

RCA Review, published quarterly by RCA, 75 Varick Street, New York. See back issues.

Radio-Craft and *Radio and Television,* both publications of Hugo Gernsback, 25 West Broadway, New York. For serviceman, experimenter, and amateur.

Radio Daily, trade paper published daily. Main office, 1501 Broadway, New York. See annual yearbooks.

Television, A Struggle for Power by Waldrop and Borkin. Morrow, New York, 1938. Social aspects.

Television Broadcasting by Lenox Lohr. McGraw-Hill, New York, 1940. Legal and economic aspects particularly.

Television—Today and Tomorrow, by Lee de Forest. Dial Press, New York, 1942. Sketch of technical side.

The Movies Come From America, by Gilbert Seldes. Scribner's, New York, 1937. History of American movies.

The Nature of Television Programs, by Gilbert Seldes. See *Annals.*

Glossary

AUDIO—From Latin, "I hear." All television broadcasting is roughly divided in two parts, the part concerning sound, and the part concerning sight. The sound part is called the *audio*. The sight end is called the *video*, from the Latin, "I see."

CATHODE RAY—A long, thin stream of electrons, emitted in a definite direction by a cathode. In the cathode ray tube —usually a sealed glass tube from which the air has been removed—the cathode ray (electron stream) is emitted by the cathode, which is the "firing chamber" of the electron gun. The two other main parts of the electron gun are the shield and anode, which are, in effect, the "barrel" of the electron gun. The cathode ray (electron stream) strikes the screen at the far end of the tube. This screen is composed of fluorescent material—phosphorescent material is sometimes included. When the cathode ray impinges on this screen, it sets up a physical reaction which causes the particular spot struck by the beam to become luminescent. The cathode ray may be made to trace any desired pattern of the screen by aiming (deflecting) it, by the use of electromagnetic or electro-static force. The electrons of the cathode ray are susceptible to these forces.

CHANNEL—The wave lengths, the "space," allotted to any radio or television transmitter for its use. The aerial equivalent of a wire linking your telephone with all the other tele-phones in the neighborhood.

CYCLE—One complete alternation of a current. Each cycle consists of a "positive" and a "negative" half-cycle—indi-cated by the signs plus and minus.

DEFINITION—The amount of detail in a picture—governed by the number of "picture elements" in each picture, and the number of pictures shown per second. The television picture is divided up into a number of horizontal lines, con-taining high lights, shadows, and half-tones. If a picture is divided into a large number of lines, it will have finer tex-ture and more detail than a picture which is divided into a smaller number of lines. High-definition pictures a few years ago were considered to be pictures with at least 240 lines of definition. But standards have improved, and now a pic-ture is not generally thought of as high definition unless it is a good 375 lines or more.

ELECTRO-MAGNETIC—Referring to a magnetic field pro-duced by an electric current. See date peg of 1819, in Chap-ter Five. Compare with electro-static.

ELECTRON GUN—See under CATHODE RAY.

ELECTRO-STATIC—Referring to an electric charge, as dis-tinct from the flow of an electric current. The action of a condenser, of a Leyden jar, or the mosaic in an iconoscope camera is electro-static. Compare with electro-magnetic, referring to magnetic field produced when a current moves through a conductor.

FLUORESCENCE—The physical property of certain sub-stances of giving off light different from their own, only during period of exposure to certain rays of the spectrum. Compare with luminescence and phosphorescence.

INVENT—To invent, a verb, meaning to find out, to orig-
inate, to devise, to frame in the mind. Often misused in
history books. People are credited with *inventing* things, and
often it looks as though they created their invention out of
nothing, starting from scratch. Actually, most inventions
are based on previous knowledge and inventions. For instance, Edison did not "invent" the incandescent light bulb
all by himself. It was based on many previous inventions, to
which he added his own skill, and taking all the existing
bits of information he put them together in the right combination and produced the light bulb.

LINES OF FORCE—The imaginary "lines" along which the
attraction of electric or magnetic force is applied. An expression used to visualize an invisible phenomenon. Refer
back to ELECTRO-STATIC and ELECTRO-MAGNETIC.
See date peg of 1831 in Chapter Five.

LUMINESCENCE—A general term applying to an emission
of light, not caused directly by incandescence (heating).
Therefore, it applies to light occurring at low tempera-
tures—and can apply to both phosphorescent and fluorescent
light.

MOSAIC—Photo-sensitive plate inside the iconoscope, the retina of the camera. See Chapter Eleven.

PHOSPHORESCENCE—The property of continuing to give
off a faint light in the dark, *after* exposure to light rays.
(Distinguished from Fluorescence.)

PHOTO-ELECTRIC—Referring to the phenomenon in which
rays of light release electrons from a substance. A photo-
electric cell is a device which gives a varying electric current in response to the variations of the light rays falling
upon it. (Selenium is no longer used in television work as
its action is too sluggish.)

STATIC—Electric interference, familiar to radio listeners as unwanted noises. Usually caused by discharge of electrostatic charges. It usually appears on television screen as specks in the picture. Actually there is little static interference on the ultra-short waves used by television, and it is usually man-made—automobile spark plugs or diathermy machines.

ULTRA-SHORT WAVES—Same as ultra-high frequencies. Wave lengths which are below 10 meters. (A wave length of 10 meters is the same thing as a frequency of 30 megacycles, or 30,000,000 cycles.) Ultra-short waves are used for transmission of television programs. There is a large range of frequencies available in this region, and television needs about 6,000,000 cycles for each station. The average radio station only needs 10,000 cycles. One television station needs as much "room" in the spectrum as the entire standard broadcast band—570 kilocycles to 1570 kilocycles—*multiplied by six.*

INDEX

INDEX

247